Yorkshire Dales Textile Mills

A history of all the textile mills in the
Yorkshire Dales
from 1784 until the present day

George Ingle

Published by Royd Press
The Book Case
29 Market Street
Hebden Bridge
West Yorks.
HX7 6EU
www.bookcase.co.uk

Cover photograph: Gayle Mill, near Hawes - George Ingle

Cover design: Kate Claughan

ISBN: 978-1-907197-00-0

For Isaac.

I hope that someday he will discover the Dales.

By the same author:

Yorkshire Cotton, Preston. 1997

Textile Manufacture in Keighley (John Hodgson, Keighley, 1879). Facsimile reprint with an introduction and index by Gillian Cookson and George Ingle (Stamford, 1999)

Marriner's Yarns, Lancaster. 2004

Sources and Acknowledgements

In writing this book I have drawn on the work and help from a number of people with considerable local and specialist knowledge. These include Chris Aspin, whose book *The Water Spinners* details his monumental search for early Arkwright-type cotton spinning mills. We have enjoyed some profitable fieldwork together as well as being able to share information. Kate Mason's books on Addingham have supplied the basis for the entries relating to Addingham and form a comprehensive account of a Yorkshire mill village. No account of hand knitting in the northern Dales can ignore Marie Hartley and Joan Ingleby's book *The Old Hand-Knitters of the Dales.* Monika Butler and colleagues from a WI class in Embsay have been very helpful in providing information about Embsay mills. Their files can be seen in Embsay Library and Monika kindly allowed me to use illustrations, maps and photographs she has collected. Michael Gill and colleagues from the Northern Mine Research Society have been most generous in sharing their data about the occupations of the inhabitants of villages in or near the Dales mining fields. Some interesting facts about the introduction of power-loom weaving into Dales mills have emerged from this information. Jo Light and other volunteers at the Upper Wharfedale Folk Museum in Grassington kindly allowed me to copy some of their photographs of Linton Mill and Grassington Low Mill. Maureen Lamb's inspiring book *The Story of Farfield Mill Restoration* details the struggle to obtain funding to restore Farfield Mill, near Sedbergh, and open it as a craft and heritage centre.

Peter Solar, from the Vrije Universiteit Brussel, has freely shared information about the early flax-spinning firms in Yorkshire and the incidence of bankruptcy amongst early cotton-spinning firms. I hope that the information I have given him has been equally beneficial.

As this is not intended as a scholarly work, detailed references have been omitted, though some key references have been included with the summary. However, the Leeds newspapers the *Leeds Intelligencer* and the *Leeds Mercury* have been a most important source, particularly for the early period up to about 1850. The precise references to mills and machinery have been taken from these papers and often relate to firms which failed, as their assets were then advertised for sale by their creditors and the mill to let by the owner. Insurance records from the Sun Fire Office and Royal Exchange Fire Office provided valuable information about the relative size of mills up to about 1815, but local offices then started to take the risks. For instance, the Leeds & Yorkshire Assurance Company was set up in the 1820s with prominent mill owners such as John Birkbeck from Settle, Robinson Chippendale from Skipton and Thomas Mason from Gargrave as shareholders. The policy registers of the national companies can be found in the Guildhall Library, London.

Parliamentary Papers, particularly the Factories Enquiry Commission report published in 1834, give information about several mills. Trade directories, published at various times, are useful, but have to be treated carefully. Information could be out of date or taken from a rival's publication. Some company records survive and these have been used where possible. The most valuable are those, not from textile firms, but from Kirkstall Forge and Hattersleys of Keighley, who supplied iron in various forms, or machined parts to mills throughout the Dales.

Increasingly locally based web sites are adding industrial history pages to the description of their town or village and these have been drawn on where relevant. Local history is ever popular and books and pamphlets based on places such as Hebden and Kettlewell give information about the textile mills on their streams. Snippets of information have been gleaned from these and many other sources. Topographical works published over the last century or so have been used as well as more recent features in the *Yorkshire History Quarterly* magazine published by Procter History in Settle. More detail about Ingleton, Clapham and Wharfe Mills can be found in back copies of the YHQ. The editors share my enthusiasm for local history.

The North Craven Heritage Trust publishes an annual Journal and the Trust has kindly allowed me to quote from past articles and use illustrations of mills in the area taken from the Journal. The Sedbergh and District History Society has a valuable archive of articles, documents and photographs and I am grateful for permission to use extracts. G E Brown & Son of Low Row, near Richmond, kindly allowed me to use some old photographs of Haverdale Mill before it was demolished.

The Yorkshire Dales National Park Authority made their database of mills taken from the first 6″ Ordnance Survey maps available to me and drew my attention to the two buildings used for silk processing in Wensleydale.

The librarians at Ilkley Public Library and Keighley Reference Library, as usual, have been helpful in providing access to some of the rare books in their collections.

The photographs and illustrations have been accumulated over fifty years. Most of the modern photographs have been taken by the author, but copies of old photographs and illustrations have come from many sources. Local historians and the keepers of local collections, such as the ones in Grassington and Sedbergh, have been most generous in giving me the opportunity to take copies from their archives. Don Barrett from The Addingham Civic Society kindly allowed me to copy some of the photographs the Society holds, taken by Hilda Holmes many years ago. Some of the photographs I have used have obviously been copied many times and the source of the original has been lost over the years. I am grateful to all those, whose generosity in providing photographs and illustrations has added to the interest of this book. If I have infringed copyright by accident in using these I can only apologise.

Finally I would like to thank Felicity Potter and Kate Claughan from Royd Press for their thoroughly professional approach in preparing the text and illustrations for this book. Their unstinted help and encouragement has helped me along the way from the original idea to the book you have in your hands.

Contents

List of illustrations

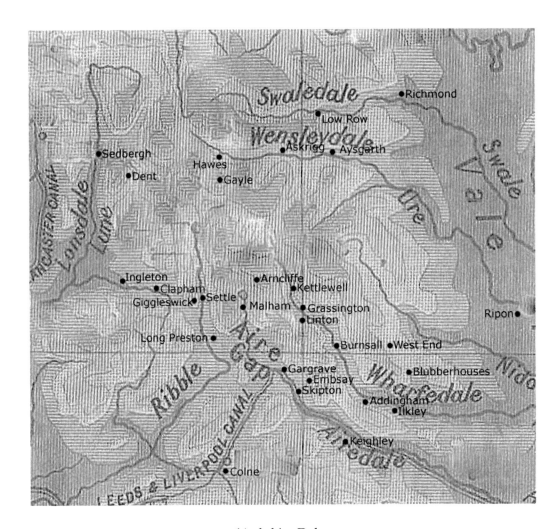

Yorkshire Dales

INTRODUCTION

A few years ago I wrote a book on the early Yorkshire cotton industry covering the period from 1780 to about 1835. Many of the mills I listed were built in the Yorkshire Dales. However, I was aware that from 1787 onwards, worsted and then flax mills were also being constructed in the same area. In addition many of the mills which were first built to spin cotton were eventually re-equipped to spin other yarns such as worsted, wool, flax and silk. In later years power-loom weaving was added to some of the mills and eventually a few processed man-made fibres. The aim of this book is to describe the general background to the establishment and purpose of all these mills as well as providing what details are available about each one.

When we think of the Yorkshire Dales today, we do not immediately associate them with the textile industry. That industry we see as being responsible for the growth of the major towns and cities of West Yorkshire, perhaps remembering that in the heyday of the industry Bradford was nicknamed 'Worstedopolis'. Halifax, Huddersfield and Keighley, with Leeds as the centre of the clothing trade, all come to mind as being the places heavily dependent on textiles until recent years. We also do not think of the Aire Valley, Calderdale or the Holme Valley as being Yorkshire dales, but obviously they are. We have come to see the industrial areas as very separate from rural areas. However, if we look closely at the distribution of industry in the old West Riding, we can see that, for example, outposts of the worsted industry existed in Otley, Addingham and Linton within living memory. Similarly the proximity of the Lancashire cotton industry meant that Skipton and Gargrave had extensive cotton mills well into the twentieth century.

One problem associated with writing about the Yorkshire Dales is exactly what area should be included. The original idea was to include only those mills within the boundaries of the Yorkshire Dales National Park, but that is a little too restrictive for my purposes, as a number of urban areas were deliberately excluded from the Park. Also there existed a number of textile mills just outside the boundaries which are interesting and help to build a more complete picture of how the textile industry developed in the Dales. One of my heroes is Arthur Raistrick, who wrote widely on the history and geology of the Dales. In his book, *Old Yorkshire Dales*, first published in 1967, he defined the Yorkshire Dales as the area between the river Aire in the south and Stainmore in the north, just to the south of the road from Barnard Castle to Appleby. The eastern boundary was where the Dales opened out onto the Vale of York, and he accepted the western boundary of the National Park. He used modern roads, such as the A65, to delineate the area he wished to include so that Skipton and Settle could be added as they are not within the National Park. However, this is a little too broad for my purpose.

The boundaries of Yorkshire itself have changed over the years, particularly with local government reorganisation in 1974. Those changes I have ignored, as the story of the growth and eventual decline of the textile industries in the Dales, I think, needs to include the textile mills around Sedbergh and Dent, which link with both the Kendal area and the upper reaches of Wensleydale and Swaledale. My boundaries to the north and east are simple, but with one exception. They are the boundaries of the National Park. In taking these boundaries some interesting mills are excluded and the linen industry based on Knaresborough is largely ignored. Flax-spinning mills existed in places like Mickleton, near Romaldkirk, where sewing thread was spun by Messrs Kidd & Dalton before 1832, and still in old Yorkshire, but to the north of Barnard Castle. To the east, mills, mainly spinning flax, operated from Richmond in the north to Thorner in the south. Nidderdale and the Washburn Valley provided sites for many of these mills, several of them extensive and operating for a century or more. The detailed story of this section of the Yorkshire flax industry has yet to be told along with the other concentrations round Leeds and Barnsley. However, the Washburn Valley has been included because of the special interest of the mills there and the usual assumption that it is a typical Yorkshire Dale and it is a popular walking area.

The south provides a few problems as there is only the artificial boundary between the National Park and the outliers of the West Riding textile area. Immediately to the south of what we think of as the Yorkshire Dales, the river Aire runs through modern Keighley, which was a major textile town but would not be considered to be in the Dales. The Aire Valley perhaps illustrates a modern division between the Dales and industrial West Yorkshire. We now see them as very different places and yet, at the end of the eighteenth century, or even the nineteenth century, those divisions were not so apparent. The stream which emerges from the foot of Malham Cove is Malham Beck, eventually becoming the River Aire, and we call the first few miles of the valley south to Gargrave, Malhamdale. Visitors throng to this Dale every year, little realising the number of textile mills which were built to take advantage of the power from the river. A few hundred metres from Malham Cove, between there and Malham village, there was a three-storey cotton mill. Just downstream from Malham there were more mills at Kirkby Malham, Airton, Bell Busk, Eshton and a further three at Gargrave. Skipton, also on the Aire, claims to be the gateway to the Dales, but was a textile town where large mills still dominate the town though no longer in use. However, it could be argued that as the river Aire is followed to the south-west, the mill villages and towns leading to Keighley are really part of a more industrialised zone. A line has to be drawn somewhere, so Skipton and mill villages such as Bradley and Cononley are excluded. To the south-east, mills on or near the Park boundary at Embsay, Eastby and Draughton have been included, as have the mills in Addingham. To include Addingham may seem odd, but the Park boundary runs less than a kilometre from Addingham High Mill and Addingham has an interesting industrial history with links both north into the Dales and south to Bradford.

For many people, a visit to the Dales involves driving north-west along the modern A65 by the rivers Aire and Ribble towards Ingleton. The main rivers here, and also their tributaries, provided many sites for early mills. For part of the way the Park boundary follows this road, but the deviations create difficulties for my story. All the mills within a mile or so of the A65 have therefore been included as far as Westhouse Mill to the west of Ingleton.

Introduction

Though the purpose of this book has been to account for all the textile mills in the Yorkshire Dales from their construction to their demise, the emphasis is on their early years. This is for two reasons. Firstly, the reason for a mill in what today is a remote area arouses considerable interest. Why should mills have been built at Arncliffe, Gayle, Blubberhouses or near Low Row in Swaledale? Why did people at the time make serious decisions to invest large capital resources in these new enterprises? Why did this early industrialisation of the Dales take place? The second reason is that more information often exists about the early years of many of the mills than their later years. Observers commented on these new developments in the 1780s and 1790s. A century later the few remaining mills in the Dales were on the fringe of the huge West Riding and Lancashire textile industries and references are hard to find.

SECTION ONE

Textiles in the Yorkshire Dales in 1780

In 1975, David Jenkins, writing about the mechanisation of the early West Riding wool textile industry, summarised the links between the Riding's textile industries.

It could be argued that the textile industries of the region should be considered as a whole and not in terms of their different branches. Their mills and factories and, to some extent, their machinery were very similar and there was considerable movement of entrepreneurship, labour and capital between them. It is hoped, in due course, that similar studies of Yorkshire flax and cotton will be prepared.

The story of the early cotton industry in Yorkshire has been attempted, but the extensive flax industry which occupied thousands of people from Cleveland in the north to Barnsley in the south has yet to be covered. However, David Jenkins's remarks apply most aptly to the textile mills in the Dales. Many of the early mills were used at various times to spin both cotton then worsted, or cotton then flax, or sometimes all three. In addition some went on to spin silk and man-made fibres. The main purpose of this work, therefore, is to trace and describe all the power-driven textile mills in the Dales and how they were used during the few or many years they ran.

By the end of the eighteenth century men, women and children throughout the entire West Riding, including the Dales, were occupied in the various stages of producing cloth or, in some areas, knitted garments. Until 1780, apart from some basic processes involved with the preparing and finishing of woollen cloth, all textile production in Yorkshire was based on hand tools and hand-operated machines. For the most part these processes were carried out in the workers' own homes or in adjoining buildings. The change came when Low Mill in Keighley began preparing and spinning cotton yarn on machinery made and operated under a licence granted by Richard Arkwright and his partners. Cotton was the newcomer, which led the way in power-driven spinning and later power-loom weaving. Wool and flax followed, which was to be expected as they had been established successfully in Yorkshire for many centuries. The different nature of the three fibres provided immense difficulties for the early machine makers who struggled to invent and, more usually, adapt, the early preparing and spinning machines. Since cotton was the easiest to process, the cotton machines provided the starting point for those who wanted to prepare and spin worsted and woollen yarn and later to use power-looms. It was a similar story for the flax industry although the nature of the flax fibres necessitated some additional processes.

The new machines not only eventually replaced the hand machines, but also the local self-sufficiency among the isolated Dales communities. Writing about Littondale, and referring to the end of the eighteenth century, a local man described how almost all clothing was made locally: coarse woollen vests, coarse woollen cloth, straw hats and coarse linen garments. Stockings and gloves were made from wool which never left the valley. Later, when cotton yarn was produced at Arncliffe Mill in Littondale, 'nearly every cottage had a loom in it, at which the mistress and daughters took their turn to weave a piece of cotton consisting of some thirty yards. It was collected from the different houses by a factor'.

Painstaking examination of parish records gives numbers of woolcombers in Aysgarth in the early 1800s, weavers in Burnsall from the early 1700s, linen weavers in Conistone again from the early 1700s and weavers in Linton and Kettlewell over the same periods. However, the impact of the new mills can be seen with William Broadley of Grassington, a rover of cotton, recorded in 1805.

The industrialization of the Yorkshire Dales by the textile industries provides an interesting picture of at least four overlapping areas related to major outside centres and I will consider each in turn. These four outside centres were Bradford, Manchester, Knaresborough and Kendal with a possible fifth at Barnard Castle. The old self-sufficiency of spinning wool and flax on a domestic scale to provide cloth for basic garments by local people was superseded by purpose-built mills and workshops from the 1780s. The West Yorkshire worsted industry had needed domestic workers, particularly spinners, in the Dales for many years. Mechanisation brought a continuation of links with Bradford, with the first worsted mill in Yorkshire built in Addingham in 1787. Other worsted mills in the Dales followed before any were built in Bradford. Cotton spinning had started even earlier with a twenty-year boom in mill-building from Sedbergh in the north to Addingham in the south. Eventually the completion of the Leeds and Liverpool Canal gave Skipton a direct connection with the cotton centres in Lancashire although not with the commercial centre of Manchester. Airedale, Wharfedale and parts of Ribblesdale were then given over to cotton, mainly yarn spinning, but with some cotton weaving in certain places. The third area to the east, including Nidderdale and the Washburn valley, became part of the Yorkshire linen industry. This stretched from Cleveland to Barnsley, but the local centre was Knaresborough where the local weavers took yarn from the Dales mills. Some mills changed between worsted, cotton and flax depending on their relative profitability. Swaledale and Wensleydale, together with the area round Sedbergh and Dent, were also involved with the worsted trade, but regarded Kendal as their major commercial centre. The mills in that locality spun yarn for knitted goods with a large proportion of the local population engaged in hand-knitting. Another type of yarn, often from the same mills, was used for the local carpet trade centered on Barnard Castle. For example, there was a woollen and worsted mill at Bowes in the 1840s which produced yarn for Monkhouse & Sons who were carpet manufacturers in Barnard Castle. The eventual specialization of the Dales mills in defined geographic areas was not always uniform however, as we shall see later with accounts of individual mills.

The approximate dates when mill or factory production of yarn and cloth made from the three fibres started in the Dales are summarised below. These are the general dates when successful production was started by a few firms which led the way. The advantages they had by being first could lead to commercial fortune, but it was not always so obvious. The change from the well established methods of hand production took many years to achieve and resulted in a great deal of hardship for those whose jobs disappeared. It is important to note that the mechanization of the main textile processes did not happen overnight, but over a period of about 100 years, with the development of new machines causing severe bottlenecks in other stages of manufacture. The resulting pressure could provide real incentives to innovate.

Start of Mill Production in the Yorkshire Dales
Spinning: Cotton – 1784; Worsted – 1787; Flax – 1795; Wool c.1820
Weaving: Cotton – 1826; Worsted c.1835; Flax – 1835; Wool c.1850

The rate of change to full factory production from the time when the innovators entered the markets varied for a number of reasons. The cost of building or renting one of the new mills and the further cost of making or buying the new machinery was one. The scale of production was higher which meant that more working capital was also required and this could exceed the level of fixed capital. The early machines were often crude, were difficult to set up and turned out a product which could, at times, be little better than that produced by a hand-operated machine. In addition, some of the first machines, which were often unimproved for a number of years, might produce only low quality yarn or cloth on which there was little profit. On the other hand, the new machines in the hands of certain individuals brought high profits which encouraged others to enter the industry. Possibly the main reason for a slow movement to factory methods, but not for cotton spinning, was that in Yorkshire highly-developed hand-powered systems had evolved for producing yarn and cloth from wool and flax. Complex organizations, together involving thousands of people over long distances, were in place and were very successful. These systems were well established by 1780 and only slowly gave way. Domestic production of worsted and linen cloth thus continued alongside factory production, with the regional specialisations which existed pre-1780 still in place by 1850. The

Yorkshire Dales were an integral part of the West Yorkshire worsted industry well before industrialisation. The carriage of wool and yarn across this area then meant that no stream or valley seemed too remote for the location of a mill.

As far as possible I have tried to avoid technical terms, but it might be useful to explain the basic processing of raw wool, cotton and flax into cloth. The essential processes are to bring together enough single fibres so that they can be twisted together to form yarn. This then needs to be divided into the warp which runs the length of the piece of cloth, and weft which runs from side to side. The weft was traditionally taken from side to side with a shuttle. Next time you are walking in the Dales and find some wool snagged on a fence try pulling it out (drawing) and twisting it. You will find that the fibres catch on each other, and if you continue drawing and twisting you will finish up with a length of thread.

Wool, as it comes from the sheep, is dirty and of different fibre lengths. The longer fibres are separated by combing. This was the last major process to be mechanised and until the 1850s was a hard and unpleasant job using pairs of wooden combs with long steel spikes which were heated in charcoal comb-pots. Cotton is cleaner, but needs to be carded to start to bring the fibres parallel with each other. Spinning involves drawing out the fibres and twisting them together. The longer each individual fibre is, the easier it is to spin, the smoother the yarn, and the finer the cloth.

Wool and Worsted

It is important to distinguish between the worsted and woollen industries, their raw materials, processes and the cloth they produced. In addition the organization of domestic manufacture differed for the two industries. Geographically they overlapped and they both used sheep's wool with the short fibres going to the woollen trade and the longer fibres to the worsted. At a time when Yorkshire accounted for more than half the production of woollen cloth in England, and most went for export, production was, with some exceptions, still in the hands of small manufacturers elsewhere and did not impact on the Dales. Clothiers in the woollen industry usually operated in a small way with the help of their family, some employees and apprentices. They carried out the various stages of manufacture and sold the fulled but unfinished cloth to a merchant or at one of the Cloth Halls. This important industry was concentrated around Leeds and the Upper Calder Valley. Cloth Halls had been built early in the century at Wakefield and Leeds with others at Huddersfield (1766), Penistone (1768), Bradford (1773), Gomersall (1774), enlarged at Leeds (1774) and Halifax (1779). These markets for woollen and later worsted cloth were used by the local manufacturers, who were part of the 'dual economy'. This meant that they also frequently practised small-scale farming to both feed their families and offset the uncertainty of the cloth trade. The land provided pasture for a few head of cattle and a horse and also the necessary area for tentering cloth.

Essential for the production of woollen cloth were water-powered fulling mills which were used to thicken and strengthen the woollen cloth. These had belonged for centuries to the manor or estate. In 1780 fulling mills were concentrated in the Huddersfield and Saddleworth area, along the Aire and Calder valleys and into Wharfedale. These mills were sometimes available for anyone to use, as in the past, but sometimes the property of individuals. By 1800 most had been converted to scribbling and carding woollen cloth and, as power was available, these later often became the buildings or sites for the new spinning or weaving mills. Few of these mills existed in the Yorkshire Dales in the period we are considering. However, as we shall see, a few Dales mills serving the hand-knitting trade did have fulling stocks to shrink and thicken sweaters, socks and other garments.

Although there was considerable overlap between the wool and worsted areas, the homes of the worsted manufacturers were concentrated around Bradford, Halifax and Keighley. Their need for labour meant that the hand spinners in the Yorkshire Dales were an essential part of the industry. By 1770 the production of worsted cloth in the Riding had equalled that of East Anglia in quantity, if not quality. From then on three trends were apparent. Firstly spinning was mechanised from the late 1780s and took place in factories. Secondly, the East Anglian industry based on Norwich declined and lastly Bradford became the centre of the worsted industry in the country. Yorkshire produced worsted cloth of low to middle quality for which there was the largest demand, particularly with the rising population that needed cheap clothing. The organisation of domestic worsted production was based on the assumption that one comber would supply fourteen spinners, who in turn would supply three to four weavers. James, writing in 1857, described the organisation of the old domestic worsted industry in the following way:

The work was entirely domestic, and its different branches widely scattered over the country. First, the manufacturer had to travel on horseback to purchase his raw material amongst the farmers, or at the great fairs held in those old towns that had formerly been the exclusive markets, or, as they were called, 'staples' of wool. The wool safely received was handed over to the sorters, who rigorously applied their gauge of required staple, and mercilessly chopped up by shears or hatchet what did not reach their standard, as wool fit only for the clothing trade. The long wool then passed into of the hands of the combers; and having been brought back to them in the combed state, (technically called 'top'), was again carefully packed, and strapped on the back of the sturdy horse, to be taken into the country to be spun. For this end, the West-Riding manufacturer had not only to visit the villages in the immediate neighbourhood of Halifax, Bradford &c., but used periodically to traverse the romantic hills and dales of Craven. Here, at each village he had his agents, who received the wool, distributed it amongst the peasantry, and received it back as yarn. The machine employed was still the old one-thread wheel; and in summer weather, on many a village green or hill-side, might be seen the housewives plying their busy trade, and furnishing to the poet the vision of 'Contentment spinning at the cottage door'. Returning in safety with his yarn, the manufacturer had now to seek out his weavers, who ultimately delivered to him his camblets, or russels, or serges, or tammies, or calimancoes (such were then the names of the leading fabrics,) ready for sale to the merchant, or delivery to the dyer.

The worsted manufacturers, as we have seen above, controlled production on an out-work system using spinners and weavers over large distances. Again, James, writing in 1857 about the worsted industry around Bradford towards the end of the eighteenth century, described the large number of spinners and hand weavers who worked in such villages of Allerton, Thornton and Wilsden. In good weather the spinners took their wheels outside and gathered together to talk as they spun. 'The average earnings of spinners at this period did not exceed sixpence a day, but the labour was light and cheerful.'

Despite the large numbers of spinners, both in the town of Bradford and in the outlying villages, not enough yarn was produced to meet the growing demand so the worsted manufacturers had to look elsewhere.

But all the exertions of the home spinners were insufficient to supply the ever-increasing demand by the weaver for yarn, and large quantities were spun in the district of Craven, and the valleys of North Yorkshire. In these localities, a strict system of inspection was enforced to prevent fraud and the production of inferior yarn. The gains to the poor agricultural labourer from this source were, in that period of low wages and dear food, of vital importance. His children, when of sufficient age to turn the one-thread wheel, were taught the art, and practised it at home, or else went to a spinning school, where the ancient dame taught them reading and spinning, and allowed them a weekly sum for their labours.

Our current thinking regarding the siting of the textile industry is usually based on mechanized production, whereas in the eighteenth century the Dales were an essential part of the whole domestic system. Transport to the more remote areas, though, was a problem until better roads were made.

Then the mode of conveyance, mostly by long trains of pack-horses, and in other cases by stage-waggons, was extremely slow and expensive, and increased greatly the obstacles which manufacturers in those times had to surmount. The formation of turnpike roads in Yorkshire during the latter part of the century, the widening and repairing of the highways which then took place, the mighty undertaking of the Leeds and Liverpool Canal formed a trunk communication from the east to the west sea and intersected the spinning country of Craven ... gave an impulse to trade in these districts, and rendered its transactions much less tedious and uncertain.

James went on to explain:

For spinning, the whole range of Yorkshire, and some parts of Lancashire, Cheshire, Derbyshire, and Westmoreland, were more or less engaged. One manufacturer chose, as his peculiar ground, Wensleydale or Swaledale; another, the forest of Knaresborough; others, various parts of Craven and Lancashire ... To show the large number of persons employed in the northern valleys of England, I have before me an account of the drawback allowed to forty-four persons who followed the business of combing wool, in Wensleydale, in 1792. Notwithstanding the multitudes employed in spinning, there was an insufficient supply of yarn, especially about the year 1780.

As well as the turnpike roads, the Leeds and Liverpool Canal, built between 1774 and 1816, was open far enough to be of benefit to Bradford worsted manufacturers before machine-spun yarn became readily available. James describes the putting-out process with particular reference to the Yorkshire Dales, using an account from Thomas Crossley, of Bradford:

... in putting out wool to spin we sent a pack of tops at once to Skipton by the canal. A boat came on purpose for the tops of various people. The pack was generally consigned to a shopkeeper or small farmer; the former the oftenest, because it brought custom to his shop. He had for putting out a halfpenny per pound. We had spinning done in Lancashire as far as Ormskirk; in Craven, and at Kirkby Lonsdale; in Wensleydale, Swaledale, and other parts of North Yorkshire. Much difficulty was experienced with the yarn; we had to sort it, and from the same top there would be yarn as thick as sixteens and as small as twenty-fours, shewing the difference in spinners. For a pound of twenties we gave on an average from ninepence to a shilling, and a good spinner from Monday morning to Saturday night might earn two shillings and sixpence a week.

Similarly, Robert Heaton, of Ponden near Keighley, sent his agent to deliver wool and collect yarn from Long Preston, Giggleswick and Rathmell in the 1760s. Hand spinners in the Dales were supplying yarn to the Bradford worsted industry as well as providing for the local hand-knitting trade.

.

The Worsted Acts

As the various stages of production of worsted cloth were usually carried out well away from the manufacturer's premises, there was the possibility of workers stealing small quantities of both wool and yarn. The wool-combers could embezzle small amounts of raw wool which was weighed out to them. Hand-spinners could keep a little of the yarn they had prepared, and hand-weavers might not use all of the yarn they were given. Though there had been previous legislation to combat these crimes, it was rarely enforced. Manufacturers who sought to use the law against their combers, spinners and weavers found that word spread and no-one would work for them. Because of the weakness of the law, fraudulent practices spread and many manufacturers were affected. The manufacturers in the West Riding, Lancashire and Cheshire therefore asked for legislation which resulted in the Worsted Acts of 1777. Besides the intended outcome, the Acts provide a useful picture of the industry and its geographic base. They should also be seen as the first example of an industry-based police-type supervision.

A committee was set up to enforce the Acts and this committee of twenty-seven people appointed inspectors to detect and prosecute offenders. The cost of the committee and inspectors was met from the tax on soap which was used to wash wool. Figures relating to the 'drawback' of the tax on soap have since been used to establish the relative scale of the industry and its location. At the first meeting of the worsted committee held at the Talbot Inn, Halifax on 9th June 1777 the region was divided into eight districts with one or more manufacturers representing each district.

For Yorkshire these were:
Halifax, and the several Yorkshire manufacturers who
usually attend that market   6
Bradford, and the like   4
Leeds, and its neighbourhood   2
Wakefield, etc   2
Huddersfield, etc   1
Keighley, etc   1
Skipton and Craven   1
Ripon and that part of the north   1
                                                                ───
                                                                18

A further nine representatives were selected for Lancashire and Cheshire.

The representatives for the Dales area were William Alcock for Skipton and Craven and Richard Brown for Ripon. Henry Alcock was a lawyer in Skipton and an investor, often with the Birkbecks, in a number of enterprises such as lead mines, turnpike roads and textile mills. Later in June the committee resolved that seven inspectors be appointed to carry out the purposes of the committee and each was allocated a district. However, the system of surveillance by the inspectors of the Worsted Committee, followed by prosecution for offences, took time to get established, as did the drawback system for the duty on soap for wool washing which financed the inspectors.

The twenty years from 1780 saw a considerable growth of textile production in the Dales. This expansion was based mainly on the cotton industry, which will be considered later, but the first changes leading towards the modern worsted industry also took place in the same area. By 1790 the worsted manufacturers in Yorkshire had ten years' experience of the impact and workings of the new cotton-spinning mills. A number of worsted manufacturers, particularly around Keighley, went into cotton spinning as an additional activity or changed over completely. Entrepreneurs started to use the same machines to spin worsted and the first worsted-spinning mill in the country was built at Dolphinholme near Lancaster in 1784. The second mill was in Yorkshire at Addingham. It was planned for cotton spinning, but John Cunliffe and John Cockshott built and installed worsted frames. These frames were similar to the machines used in the cotton trade. They were very successful and the yarn was well received on the Bradford market. Shortly after Addingham Low Mill was built in 1787, experiments started at High Mill, a mile upstream. This former corn mill was extended and a new mill built, which then was occupied by Richard Hargreaves, a cotton manufacturer, together with his partners Robert Hargreaves, William Thompson, John and William Birkbeck and Richard Smith, senior and junior. The Leeds agent of the Royal Exchange Insurance Company reported in 1789 that sheep's wool was being spun there. The Birkbecks, merchants and bankers in Settle, were eager to back new textile ventures. Robert Hargreaves was successful in overcoming difficulties with spinning, and with financial support from the Birkbecks, built a larger worsted-spinning mill at Linton, near Grassington.

The two mills at Addingham and Linton remained the only worsted-spinning mills in the Dales for several years. By 1810, it was felt that the drawback system was sufficiently well-established enough to provide figures for the volume of wool prepared at various places in Yorkshire and parts of Lancashire, though these figures should be treated with some reservation. They relate to the amount of wool combed by the domestic wool combers which would have then been spun on a hand wheel unless there was a spinning mill in the locality. Further complications could arise because some country combers, often called 'basketeers', would travel to places like Keighley to collect wool to comb. The places listed appear to modern eyes to be rather arbitrary with, for example, Manningham not included with Bradford, but the expansion of the major towns was only just beginning. The list below includes all the centres which could be classed as within the Yorkshire Dales generally together with some others for comparison. The total amount was £4,993 but included Lancashire towns such as Bacup, Bolton, Burnley and Colne.

Amount of drawback in 1810

(The figures have been rounded up or down to the nearest £)

Addingham	£157
Bedale	£1
Baildon	£24
Bingley	£159
Bradford	£851
Burtersett	£5
Burton	£12
Catterick	£3
Gayle	£10
Haworth	£382
Hawes	£6
Halifax	£257
Huddersfield	£1
Keighley	£199
Knaresborough	£3
Leeds	£354
Lothersdale	£9
Masham	£89
Otley	£4
Ripon	£5
Selby	£10
Skipton	£119
York	£18

The figures for some individual manufacturers were published, with one of the largest, Birkbeck & Co., accounting for the whole of the Skipton area's return, presumably based on the amount of wool processed for their worsted spinning mill at Linton, near Grassington. The figures were further aggregated into districts with the following results for 1810, 1815, 1820 and 1825. Bradford and Keighley have been added for comparison.

Drawback distributed to Districts

District	1810	1815	1820	1825
Bradford	£851	£1485	£2411	£5034
Keighley	£581	£764	£1178	£1937
Otley	£33	£288	£453	£922
Skipton & Addingham*	£275	£291	£172	£345
York	£204	£127	None	None

Only Skipton for 1820

The changes in these figures over fifteen years reflect the industrial adjustments that were taking place. Two of the cotton mills in Otley changed to worsted spinning, so more wool was processed there after 1810. Low Mill at Addingham, one of the largest in the area, was changed from worsted to cotton just before 1820 and the York area declined with the rise in machine spinning in the West Riding.

The use of mills in the southern and western Dales for worsted spinning at the very start of the mechanisation of the industry probably relates to the availability of water power as much as to the enterprise of local men. Eventually, after 1787, hundreds more mills were built specifically for spinning worsted in West Yorkshire but few were built in the Dales. The further growth of the industry was to be in and around Bradford, Halifax, Huddersfield and Keighley. It is difficult to select one date and one event that highlights the changes that were to come, but the building of Holme Mill in Bradford in 1800 will suffice. This first mill in the parish of Bradford was built by Ramsbotham, Swaine & Murgatroyd for worsted and cotton spinning. It might have had the dimensions of a typical Dales Arkwright mill at 32½ by 11 yards, but it had a steam engine. This, of course, was significant, as steam was the future after 1800 when the Boulton & Watt patent expired. The ability to buy an engine from a range of suppliers and access to cheap coal meant that mechanisation would be concentrated in areas away from the Dales. However, some years later, once steam power became more efficient and relatively cheaper, engines were installed in Dales textile mills to supplement water power in times of draught, but the cost of bringing in coal was always a consideration. By then, though, the new, larger mills, built to accommodate larger and more modern machines, had the advantage and they were usually in or near the new industrial towns and cities. Water power continued to be used well into the nineteenth century, but usually only in the rural areas. There are a few exceptions, though, where the water supply was substantial, for new dams to be constructed, new goits cut and new wheels installed. The weaving shed at Langcliffe, just north of Settle, was one, and in a few mills more efficient water turbines were installed, sometimes to drive the line shafting directly or by dynamos and electric motors.

Skyreholme Mill Water Wheel

The Introduction of Cotton Spinning

At the end of June 1780, power from the line shafting was applied to a series of carding, roving, drawing and spinning machines in Low Mill on the River Worth in Keighley. Partly cleaned cotton was fed on to the cards at one end and finished yarn was wound onto bobbins at the other. An initial single shift of children, working 12 hours a day, replaced the 'housewives plying their busy trade' and the textile trade in Yorkshire was to change forever. The partners at the mill who came from Lancashire, Thomas Walshman and his son Robert, along with three Clayton brothers, had experience and capital and also a licence from Arkwright and his partners to run 2,000 spindles. Some of the young workers had been to Arkwright's Cromford Mills to learn how to operate the new machines and the partners were on their way to making their fortune.

The success of Arkwright and his partners stimulated Yorkshire men and women to invest in cotton by building spinning mills in the Pennine valleys, from Sheffield in the south to Sedbergh in the north. Arkwright's rise from barber to one of the richest men in the country certainly did not go unnoticed and hundreds of people, often with no knowledge of textiles, rushed to start up in the new industry. It has been estimated that only about 20 per cent of newcomers to the cotton trade in Yorkshire knew anything about the industry while a similar percentage came from the woollen or worsted industries. Some were merchants, such as the Quaker Birkbecks of Settle, who were eager to invest in new technology. One of their partners, John Pratt of Askrigg, was a country gentleman, ex-jockey and racehorse owner. Agnes Driver, also from Askrigg took over the running of a mill after the death of her husband. Thomas Parker, a publican from Keighley, built Arncliffe Mill, set out as a cotton spinner and manufacturer and his three sons followed him, eventually running mills in Hebden, Gargrave and Keighley. The attention paid to Arkwright's activities and those of his partners, was not lost on others. In 1785 a Leeds paper reported that:

The great mechanick Arkwright was a barber in Manchester and a few years ago shaving for a penny. His astonishing machine brought him one year a revenue of £70,000 and, though he has lowered his prices to crush his rivals, his profits are yet between 40 and £50,000 a year.

Interest in Arkwright and his cotton machines was such that a showman who attended Arkwright's final trial in 1785 (he lost) bought a set and exhibited them in the Strand in London, charging one shilling to view.

Some people even ignored his patent rights and built their own mills and machinery. The appetite of Arkwright's machines for cotton and the resulting quantities of regular and evenly spun yarn available at a good price was the reward. When Arkwright lost his patent rights in 1785, the field was wide open for anyone with capital, access to land with a water course and especially, a partner with some mechanical knowledge, to become a cotton spinner.

The Introduction of Cotton Spinning

William Baynes of Embsay Kirk, near Skipton, planning a mill in Embsay in 1792, was told that 10 frames, with 72 spindles each, would spin 31 packs of cotton a year. The mill would require 120 workers at an average wage of 5/- a week. Running costs would therefore be £2,420 with a profit of £2,200. If this was typical of many people's thinking, it is little wonder that so many rushed to find partners and build a cotton spinning mill. Arkwright's water frame enabled strong cotton warps to be spun. These replaced linen warps and all cotton cloth could be woven with the weft supplied from hand-powered jennies.

The Yorkshire Dales provided ideal sites for these mills, some of the first of which were built in Wensleydale in 1784. High demand at home and abroad for cotton cloth, recent improvements to speed up the handloom and the opportunity to copy Arkwright without paying several hundred pounds for a licence led to would-be investors scouring the Dales for suitable sites. They found dozens of abandoned corn mills, where rights to the water supply, access roads, and buildings with waterwheels were waiting to be snapped up. Because the old corn mill buildings were rarely adequate they were quickly replaced or a new mill was built alongside, as at Hebden. These old mills, many of which had a history going back to medieval times, had served their local communities when oats and barley were grown in each village. Now the new turnpike roads and canals meant that cheap corn could be brought from East Yorkshire, and local agriculture changed over to pastoral farming. Today it is difficult to imagine each Dales village having an area of ploughed fields and its own corn mill to grind the oats and barley, but by 1792 a visitor to the area wrote that:

... the cotton trade, with its high pay, has put an end to all thoughts of husbandry; canals and cotton mills are the only thought.

The changes in agriculture, by accident, favoured the new mill owners in that many former agricultural labourers had to leave the land and took up employment as handloom weavers. They then were able to weave up much of the additional yarn which was being produced in the locality.

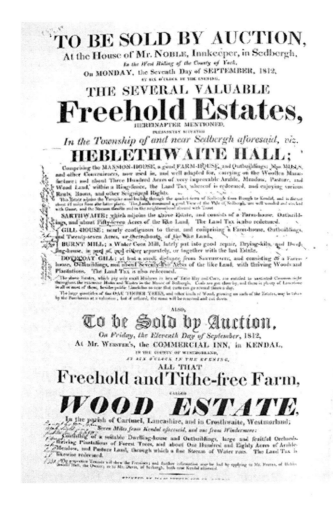

1812 Sale Notice for Hebblethwaite Hall and Mills

The Leeds papers carried numerous advertisements for corn mills, often listing their advantages if they were to be used for cotton spinning.

1784 - water corn mills to let at Settle and Giggleswick

1785 – Threshfield and Linton Mills for sale:
'Linton Mill is in the most eligible and advantageous situation for a cotton mill ... suitable buildings may be erected for the purpose.'

1785 – old corn mill for sale at Arncliffe:
'It is a very convenient situation for establishing a cotton manufactory.'

1786 – water corn mill for sale in or near Grassington
1791 – a millstead at Burnsall
'... where labour is cheap and where the children and upgrown persons are mostly in want of employment.'
1791 – site available for a cotton mill at Linton Bridge near Grassington – the site of an old fulling mill on the River Wharfe
1791 – Blubberhouses water corn mill for sale
'... near the grand road from Skipton to Knaresborough with the best of stone for building near at hand.'

The later dominance of Lancashire as the principal county for cotton spinning and weaving has overshadowed the early significance of the Yorkshire cotton industry. However, as cotton was well established in Lancashire before the introduction of mechanisation, the advance from hand production was not well received. In 1779, rioters worked their way through towns and villages destroying the larger hand machines which were thought to be taking away jobs for women and children, and burned down Arkwright's Birkacre mill. For a while mill building slowed in Lancashire. Two of the partners at Birkacre joined new partnerships in Yorkshire, John Cross, at a mill in Leeds and Thomas Walshman first at Low Mill in Keighley and then at Langcliffe Mill, near Settle.

In Section II there is a description of all the new mills. However, the scale and speed of this industrialisation of the Yorkshire Dales warrants some comment. In recognition of the growing importance of cotton weaving, the proprietors of rooms at Halifax Piece Hall changed their rules in February 1805:

Ordered
That cotton and cotton goods, may be admitted into the Hall, for the purpose of being exposed for Sale, at the usual Market Hours, subject to such Rules and Regulations as are established for the Admission and Sale of Worsted and Woollen Manufactures.

In 1837 William White's Directory of Yorkshire could confidently assert that:

...though there are within the limits of the West Riding 140 cotton mills employing about 10,000 persons, most of them are near the Lancashire border, and all of them are situated in the Wapentakes of Agbrigg, Morley and Staincliffe-and-Ewecross, extending from Saddleworth to Sedbergh, except one at Birstwith and another near Otley.

A few pages further on, cotton spinning firms were listed in many places including Addingham, Arncliffe, Hartlington and Kettlewell.

This industrialisation of the Dales did not pass without notice, particularly in the early years. The huge commercial success of Richard Arkwright and his partners was well known, but the spread of the industry to rural areas was not liked by some:

But what has completed the destruction of every rural thought, has been the erection of a cotton mill (Yore Mill) on one side, whereby prospect and quiet are destroyed: I now speak as a tourist (as a policeman, a citizen, or a statesman, I enter not the field); the people indeed are employed, but that are all abandoned to vice from the throng.

At the times when people work not in the mill, they issue out to poaching, profligacy and plunder – Sir Rd Arkwright may have introduced much wealth into his family, and into the country, but, as a tourist I execrate his schemes, which having crept into every pastoral vale, have destroyed the course and beauty of nature; why here now is a great flaring mill, whose back stream has drawn off half the water of the falls above the bridge. [Aysgarth Falls].

Child Labour

Setting up as a cotton spinner in the Dales in the 1780s and 1790s meant bringing together sufficient capital to build a mill and finance its operation, a good waterpower location and the acquisition of a work force with a number of skills. Finance could come from a wide variety of sources, hence the large number of partnerships which were formed. Frequently some of the partners had no knowledge of cotton spinning or even of any textile processes. They might be lawyers, merchants or landowners. Reliance was placed on a manager and the overlookers, or the one partner who brought some cotton expertise to the enterprise. Until steam engines became reliable and readily available with a cheap supply of coal, a good waterpower site was essential, but even then the vagaries of the Yorkshire climate and the actions of other mill owners could jeopardise the water supply. The new element in the formula for success was an adequate supply of children to operate the new machines, and, in the early years, with the new skill to do so.

Much has been written about the employment of children in the early cotton mills and much health and safety legislation we are familiar with today can be traced back to those times. The whole point of the new textile machines was that they did not rely on the skills of adults, but on being attended to by children. If a hand spinner stopped, no yarn was produced. A child spinner could watch a water frame with, say, 120 spindles run for a twelve-hour shift, and just have certain specified jobs to do. All the new mills needed these children, and their assembly at set times under the control of adults, who were not their parents, created a new industrial work force. This was an age well before compulsory schooling when the labour of children in any part of the country was essential for families to survive. Child labour was not unusual; what was unusual was the rigid way the work was organised and the dominance of the powered machine. Young people tended both carding and spinning frames, and prompting the *Leeds Mercury* of January 24, 1785, to draw attention to this new occupation.

To spin with art, in ancient times, has been
Thought not beneath the noble Dame and Queen.
From that employ our maidens had the name
Of SPINSTERS, which the moderns never claim.
But since to cards each damsel turns her mind
And to that dear delight is so inclin'd;
Change the soft name of Spinster to a harder,
And let each woman now be called a CARDER.

The growth of the use of child labour in factories continued for many years. The First Report of the Factories Inquiry Commission in 1833 had this to say:

Children employed in factories, as a distinct class, form a very considerable proportion of the infant population. We have found that the numbers so employed are rapidly increasing, not only in proportion to the increase of the population employed in manufacturing industry, but, in consequence of the tendency of improvements in machinery to throw more and more of the work upon children, to the displacement of adult labour. The children so employed are assembled together in large numbers, and in buildings of peculiar construction, which cannot be mistaken for private dwellings. Their daily entrance into and dismissal from the factories take place with the regularity of military discipline.

Since child labour was necessary for the efficient running of the new cotton mills, the owners had three choices in finding the large numbers of children required. Firstly they could build their mills in towns and villages with a good-sized population, bearing in mind that a suitable water-powered site must also be available. Country areas were thought to have the advantage of lower wages, as there was usually no competition from other mills or industries. Agriculture certainly was seen to pay low wages and landowners often feared the construction of a mill near their estate as its presence would force up wages. It was said that in the neighbourhood of Settle, labourers' wages doubled between 1783 and 1793, because of the introduction of cotton mills.

Linton Corn Mill, near Grassington, was for sale in 1786 and the sale notice covered both aspects.

Linton Mill is the most eligible and advantageous situation for a cotton mill, being so well supplied with water by the great river Wharfe, and in the centre and within a short walk of the several populous towns and villages of Grassington, Threshfield, Linton, etc where from the ringing of a bell upwards of three hundred children may be collected in less than half an hour.

Similarly land with a water supply for sale at Embsay near Skipton, also in 1786, was described in the same terms:

This stream runs copiously in the most extreme droughts and plenty of hands to attend a mill of a moderate size might be had from Embsay, Eastby and the contiguous villages.

Also a millstead at Burnsall was said to be:

… very desirable for carrying on a work of this kind to any extent being within a mile of the furthest of three villages where labour is cheap and where the children and upgrown persons are mostly in want of employment.

An advertisement for the corn mill at Coniston, between Gargrave and Hellifield, in January 1794, mentioned that:

The stream to the mill may be commodiously appropriated to spinning mills and other manufactories to which Coniston and the neighbourhood would supply sufficient spinners.

We must always remember that the population of Dales villages was much higher than it is today. The other alternative though, if enough children did not live in the area, was to persuade families to move there by providing cottages and so the concept of mill housing began. Clayton & Walshman, who started building Langcliffe Mill outside Settle in 1783, following their success with Low Mill in Keighley, placed the following advertisement in the Leeds newspapers in 1786.

Notice is hereby given that Messrs Clayton & Walshman, cotton manufacturers, in order to accommodate work people are now erecting a number of convenient cottages at Langcliffe Place, which will be ready to enter on at May Day next.

In 1843 Westhouse Mill in the Washburn Valley had 37 cottages for workpeople and other examples of rather isolated mills which had cottages built nearby were at Arncliffe, Scalegill in Malhamdale and Low Mill, Addingham.

The third alternative, which has aroused much interest over the years, was to import children specifically to work in a mill from some other part of the country. The supply of children came from parishes and workhouses in many towns and cities where they could be a burden on the rates when they were orphaned or abandoned. Overseers and workhouse governors were then tempted to send children they were responsible for to a cotton manufacturer. This saved the parish money, and they could claim that the children would be apprenticed, learn some skills, attend church and have a limited amount of schooling. The reality was often very much different and there are examples of cruel treatment by mill owners, or their overlookers, which were investigated by concerned parishes or came to light in Parliamentary enquiries.

The Leeds newspapers carried advertisements for these potential apprentices. For instance, in November 1804 children were available from Grantham:

To manufacturers
Several stout healthy boys and girls are ready to be put out as parish apprentices. For further particulars enquire of the church wardens and overseers of Grantham, in the County of Lincoln.

However, it was from London, or more precisely the parishes of Southwark and Lambeth that apprentices came to Westhouse Mill, near Blubberhouses, in the Washburn Valley. This was one of the largest mills built in the Yorkshire Dales and some details survive of the process of taking the children and how they lived and worked at the mill.

Westhouse Mill was an impressive attempt at large-scale flax spinning with weaving and finishing added later and is dealt with in more detail in Section Two. The mill was built in 1797 by several partners with money borrowed from John Greenwood of Keighley who was involved in many textile mills, although usually cotton. The original partners were Thomas Colbeck, William Holdsworth and John Holdsworth who traded as Colbeck & Co. They were soon joined by Roland Watson, a Keighley solicitor, and in 1798 they advertised for flax dressers. The isolation of the mill in Fewston parish meant that labour had to be sought from elsewhere. By 1803, children were being brought from London. In September 1803, St Mary's, Lambeth sent four girls to Westhouse Mill. In March, nine girls from St George the Martyr, Southwark were sent, followed by two more in October. Some fourteen girls and six boys made the long journey north in November; and ten years later six girls travelled to Blubberhouses from the same parish.

An indenture for one of the boys, dated the 20th of November 1804, details the apprenticeship arrangement. The churchwardens of the parish together with the overseers of the poor and with the consent of the Justices of the Peace:

... do put and place Frederick Simpson aged twelve years or thereabouts, a poor child of the said Parish Apprentice to Thomas Colbeck, Rowland Watson, Francis Watson, Jacob Wilks, John Holdsworth and William Holdsworth of Westhouse near Otley, Yorkshire, flax manufacturers, with them to dwell and serve from the Day of the Date of these presents, until the said apprentice shall accomplish his full age of Twenty-one years according to the Statute in that case made and provided: During which Term, the said Apprentice his said Masters faithfully shall serve in all lawful Businesses, according to his Power, Wit, and Ability; and honestly, orderly, and obediently in all things demean and behave himself towards his said masters...

The masters, on their part, in turn had to provide young Frederick with 'meat, drink, apparel, lodging, washing and other things necessary and fit for an apprentice'. There was also a caveat that the masters would not allow the apprentice to be a charge to the parish.

The Health and Morals of Apprentices Act of 1802 required JPs to visit textile mills which employed apprentices. Though many ignored their responsibilities, William Vavasour, Squire of Weston, near Otley, visited Westhouse Mill on many occasions. He had the power to send erring or runaway apprentices to the 'House of Correction'. In the autumn of 1815 he had to do so three times and finally early in December after a disturbance amongst the workpeople, he sent a girl to prison for the second time. The following year Thomas Colbeck, the senior partner at the mill, called on Vavasour to ask for a written testimonial that his factory was well conducted as far as the treatment of children was concerned. The reason was that a new Parliamentary Bill was being proposed to further restrict the employment of children. Vavasour gave the testimonial with 'much pleasure'. However, he was not so pleased when Colbeck and his partners were rendered bankrupt in August 1816 and doubts were cast on Thomas Colbeck's honesty.

The child apprentices at Westhouse Mill lived in two apprentice houses, one for the girls and one for the boys. These were on Hardisty Hill at Blubberhouses and were converted from cottages. Two orphans from London, who went to Westhouse Mill as pauper apprentices, later married and had a son called Robert Collyer. He became a prominent Unitarian minister in the United States and wrote extensively about his early life at the mill. His parents, Samuel Collyer and Harriet Norman were married at Fewston Church in January 1823, but soon moved to Keighley where Robert was born. When they returned to Blubberhouses, Samuel worked in the smithy at the mill while his son Robert started as a doffer in the spinning section when he was eight years old. His memories of working life at the mill stayed with him throughout his life:

[We were] … rung in at six in the morning and out at eight in the evening, with an hour for dinner and a rest. And if we got a chance to sit down for a few moments when the overlooker was not round with his leathern strap to lay on our small shoulders, while for protection we invented a code of signals to warn each other when he was coming our way; and the result of this was that the weaker children were so crippled that the memory of their crooked limbs still casts a rather sinister light for me on the scripture, 'The Lord regardeth not the legs of a man' … The quite infernal factory bell began to clang through the valley at half past five in the morning, before, as I was sure, I had been asleep an hour, so tired I was and so sure also that in all the world there could be no bell so harsh or evil in sound.

Robert originally worked from 6 in the morning till 8 at night at Westhouse Mill, with an early finish on Saturday at 6 pm. However, through legislation, hours for children aged between nine and thirteen were reduced from seventy-six to forty-eight when he was ten years old. Robert's parents did not want him to work for too many years in the mill so when he was fourteen he started an apprenticeship with the blacksmith in Ilkley.

Michael Robinson, the manager, answering the questions from the Factory Enquiry Commissioners in 1833, said mill owners

... see no need of any interference by Act of Parliament for the regulation of factory labour, further than the protection of children under twelve years of age, which certainly would be an act of greater humanity than many parents exercise towards their children. We have no doubt, if children be injured by the factory labour, it is while they are under twelve years of age, by confinement, without that free exercise they require.

In 1833 the 'Westhouse Factory Company' employed twenty-one children under twelve with those under ten earning two shillings a week (10p) and those between ten and twelve three shillings (15p).

The hours of work had been reduced from 6 am until 8 pm because trade was flat and the owners had

... been compelled to reduce the hours of labour to fifty-six hours per week, and, but for the sake of enabling the hands to get a subsistence should have reduced more time.

There was no pay for Christmas Day and the other two half-day holidays in the year were accounted for by working the dinner hour. The early finish on a Saturday was, of course, made up for by working half an hour longer each day from Monday to Friday.

The advocates of legislation to reduce working hours and improve working conditions brought forward many examples of cruelty to children whilst the apologists sought to play down the ill effects of factory work. Perhaps the strongest attempt to prejudice thinking about child labour in a Yorkshire mill relates to Westhouse Mill and appeared in a book written many years after the supposed events:

At West End, a hamlet not far from the main road from Harrogate to Skipton, lies the remains of an old woollen-mill operated by water-power. Hundreds of children from the south of England were sent to it by the magistrates, and as they died at the looms their bodies were thrown into a pit dug on the opposite side of the road. (*Curtis and Boultwood, 1965*)

Westhouse Mill was never a woollen mill and, though power-looms for weaving linen were introduced about 1839, they were usually operated by adults. The apprenticeship system had also stopped well before that date.

The Health and Morals of Apprentices Act of 1802 brought indignation from many of the Yorkshire mill owners and a meeting to 'take into consideration the best mode to be adopted for restoring the Trade to its former Freedom' was held in Keighley in February 1803. Among the fourteen mill owners who attended were William Clayton, a partner at Langcliffe Mill near Settle; Lister Ellis and his brother William, who was to be a partner at Westhouse; John Greenwood, who had provided some of the capital for the mill; and Mr Sidgwick who was a cotton spinner at Skipton and Milthrop Mill, near Sedbergh. Most of the rest were partners in mills in the Keighley Area. The group of mill owners hoped to petition the House of Commons to repeal the Act reducing the number of hours worked by children. However, their efforts had no effect and many of the local mill owners registered their mills with the Justices of the Peace. They in turn appointed one of their members and a clergyman to examine the mills once a year.

Among the 47 Yorkshire cotton mills registered under the 1802 Act were:

Anthony Fentiman's mill in Addingham
James Brown & Co's mill at Hartlington, near Burnsall
Sidgwick & Garforth's mill at Sedbergh
Walker & Co's two mills at West End in the Washburn Valley

Clayton & Walshmans's mill at Langcliffe, near Settle
J J & T Thornber's mill at Settle
Edmund Armitstead's mill at Settle Bridge
Thomas Danson & Co's mill at Bentham
Helliwell & Garforth's mill at Bell Busk

It has also been noted that Aked's at West End employed apprentices. Further mills may also have used apprentice labour, for many of the mill owners either did not bother to register or were not aware of their responsibility to do so. Smaller mills may have employed fewer than 20 workpeople and three apprentices and were therefore exempt from the cost of registering of one shilling.

John Hannam, one of the adults giving evidence to the Factory Inquiry Commissioners in 1833 and had worked at Hebden Mill, thought that there was more bad management of children in country places, such as the Dales than in the towns:

Where there is only one mill or two they are bound to put up with anything for fear of losing their work; they have that advantage, where one master does not strive against another. In Leeds, if the hands are offended in one place, they can get work in another; in the country it is the reverse; the master can make them do as he likes.

Another example of how factory children could be treated also comes from Hebden Mill and relates to how children were seen as the property of the employer.

Notice is hereby Given
That William Anthony Thomas and Samuel Sutcliffe, sons of Nancy, alias Ann Sutcliffe, late of Airton and now of Hebden, are work children in the mill of Mr William Parker, of Hebden aforesaid, Cotton Spinner, (lawfully hired) therefore any Person or Persons hiring or attempting to seduce the said children from Mr Parker's employ, before the Expiration of their Services according to Contract, will be prosecuted according to law.
Hebden Mill April 18 1807

Working conditions in mills prompted numerous protests. On January 5, 1843, the *Bradford Observer* published a letter from a reader who had seen Low Mill at Addingham working on Christmas Day, which was also a Sunday:

At my nearer approach became horror-struck to find the upper room of a large cotton factory lighted by gas, and its helpless inmates, who I afterwards learned consisted principally of girls from fourteen to eighteen, suffering the torture of protracted labour to suit the purpose of some cruel taskmaster.

When William Threlfall was charged by the Factory Inspector at Bingley Court it came to light that the girls had worked from 6 am until midnight on the Thursday and continuously from the Friday until the Sunday. Threlfall offered the excuse that he was trying to complete a large export order, but was fined £80. Overall he had a reputation as a bad employer which was not surprising.

Occasionally employers behaved generously and, in August 1814, when it appeared that the French wars were over and Napoleon had been banished to Elba, John and William Birkbeck provided a dinner of roast beef and plum pudding for 450 of their workpeople in a field next to Linton Mill. This was followed with a distribution of ale and with dancing. Thirty years previously Claytons & Walshman had provided dinner with ale and buns for the workmen and children to accompany the festivities at the opening of Langcliffe Mill near Settle.

Flax Spinning

Flax and hemp were grown throughout the lower Dales in medieval times and were spun and woven locally. One of the problems in preparing the yarn was that both flax and hemp needed to be steeped in water to separate the fibres from the rest of the plant stem. This is known as retting, but because it produces poisonous by-products, special retting pits were prepared near to streams for a supply of water, but away from houses and where cattle grazed. The banks of the excavated pits then provided a drying area for the fibres. Examples of these have been found near Draughton, Sedbergh and Burton-in-Lonsdale, though they would have been found in many other areas. To supplement the supply of local grown flax, imports from the Baltic started in the seventeenth century. During the eighteenth century this trade continued to grow with imports into Hull increasing through the expansion of the linen industry around Knaresborough. Flax could be brought by boat to a wharf just one mile downstream from Boroughbridge. The organisation of the manufacture of various types of cloth was usually divided into two parts with the heckling and spinning being the followed by weaving and bleaching.

Whitaker's *History of Craven,* published early in the nineteenth century, gives a number of examples of places where hemp and flax were grown in earlier years. One place given particular attention was Linton, which, according to Whitaker, derived its name from the amount of line or flax grown in the area, and which, 'the inhabitants spun and prepared for themselves'. Even today there is a Hemplands Cottage and Hemplands Farm near Conistone in Wharfedale.

An Act of Parliament at the end of the eighteenth century provided a bounty for the growing and preparation of hemp and flax. In 1787 this was three pence a stone for hemp and four pence a stone for flax. Claims had to be made to a JP and attested by two parish officers. In 1837 when Rawcliffe Factory, a steam-powered flax-spinning mill near Goole, was for sale, it was said to be in the centre of a district famous for the production of flax.

Transport improvements initially did little to encourage the growth of the linen industry around Knaresborough and into the eastern Dales. The Ripon Canal to the east and the Leeds and Liverpool to the west were too far away, but the general road improvements did help, particularly between Skipton and Knaresborough. However, when Newbridge Flax Mill at Wath in Nidderdale was for sale in 1824 it was said that 'the benefit of a navigable canal to Ripon, [is] of great advantage in the carriage of flax and tow from Hull for the spinning business'.

The growth of the linen trade was hampered by the same problem that faced the worsted manufacturers: the need to use the services of hundreds of hand spinners scattered over a large area and working to different standards. Mechanisation of the spinning process came first, as with cotton and worsted, while power-loom weaving followed many years later. However, the established linen manufacturers had the capital to build new spinning mills or adapt the early cotton mills to spin flax. Typical examples of conversions are Gayle Mill, near Hawes, Askrigg Mill and Low Mill at West End in the Washburn valley. The large mill near Blubberhouses called Westhouse Mill was built specifically for flax spinning in 1797. New mills in the eastern Dales and elsewhere were then able to supply a constant quality and growing volume of yarn to the hand weavers around Knaresborough. In 1810 it was reported that 1,000 linen pieces measuring 20 yards by 35 inches were manufactured in the town and neighbourhood every week.

Most of the new flax-spinning mills were in Nidderdale, and to the east and west of the A1. Those mills lie outside our area, but for many years contributed to a temporary industrialisation of small towns and villages in the same way as the early cotton mills in the Dales. Flax mills at Masham, Ripon and Thirsk as well as smaller places such as Bishop Monkton, Mickley, Rawcliffe and Winkesley were active for a number of years and formed part of an industry that ran as far north as South Stockton and Middlesborough in Cleveland on the river Tees.

A small number of mills in the western Dales were either used for flax spinning over a few years or had flax frames running alongside the other spinning machinery. Examples are Wharfe Mill, near Austwick,

Ingleton Mill and Addingham High Mill. There is only one record of the use of power-looms to weave linen in the Dales mills and the spinning machinery probably lagged behind the latest models used in the main centres of the industry. Wet spinning was gradually introduced, followed by heating the water to soften the gummy matter in the flax, thus making it possible to draw the fibres into finer yarns.

Throughout the period covered by this book, trading conditions were rarely constant. The French wars until 1815, threats of wars, tariffs, changes in fashion and changes in technology made life difficult, particularly for the firms which were undercapitalised and operated on the margins of the industry, like many in the Dales. The *Leeds Mercury* carried an editorial in October 1842 drawing attention to the imposition of recent tariffs: Russian on worsted, woollen and mixed worsted/cotton fabrics; Portuguese on woollen; French on linen and linen yarns; Belgian on linen and linen yarns and German on worsted. The tariffs on linen and linen yarn hit the flax-spinning firms in West End and many ceased trading about this time.

Silk and Rayon

Silk has always been a luxury fabric. The basic fibres have always been imported, as attempts to grow the mulberry trees, on which the silk worms or caterpillars feed, were unsuccessful in this country. The fibre can be a continuous filament where many are twisted together in a process called throwing and is the equivalent of spinning other fibres. The long silk fibres are twisted together in different ways depending on their final use. Some shorter fibres remain on the silk cocoon and these are removed by brushing and can then be spun in the normal way. This is sometimes referred to as silk waste.

During the eighteenth and nineteenth centuries, silk manufacture rose in importance, but there were changes after about 1860. The industry was very small compared with the cotton, wool and flax industries and had no geographic centre. Small pockets existed in a number of counties including Yorkshire, and several mills in the Dales were used for silk spinning. Production of silk yarn and cloth expanded until 1860, when a treaty with France allowed French silk goods to be imported without duty whilst a tariff was imposed on British goods entering France.

The spinning and weaving of silk often remained a hand industry long after water or steam power had been applied to cotton. Manually-operated winding and throwing mills, often worked by children, continued to be used. Lack of cohesion in the scattered industry with low levels of technological innovation and training again hindered progress.

After 1860 there was a decline in the production of silk cloth and many mills in Nottingham, Congleton and Macclesfield closed. However, better understanding of how to prepare, dye and finish mixed cloths resulted in an increase in the demand for silk yarn to combine with cotton. In addition, the leisured-class Victorian ladies created a demand for embroidery threads. This was the period when some large mills in the Dales changed over to spin silk and in one case, to weave silk cloth.

Two buildings in Wensleydale were built for waste silk processing, but for one of them there is little surviving evidence. Countersett Silk Mill is a small two-storey, three-bay building constructed in 1793 and originally powered by a waterwheel to drive the carding engine. It was described as 'Old Silk Mill' on the 1910 Ordnance Survey, with the ground floor as living accommodation. The first floor may have been used for processing the silk with simple hand equipment apart from the card. The other was Burtersett Candle Mill which a local historian, James Alderson, referred to as 'the old silk mill' before William Metcalfe took it over to make candles about 1850. This could also have

Burtersett Candle Mill

been used for twisting and throwing silk on basic hand machines. Unfortunately, there is no record of how the yarn was used, but examples at Burton-in-Lonsdale and Austwick would indicate that the use of silk in the Dales in the early nineteenth century was not unusual. Burton-in-Lonsdale Mill spun some silk for a few years from about 1795, alongside cotton, and Wharfe Mill, near Austwick, did the same about 1816. Nothing has been found about how the yarn was used. Local handloom weavers may have woven silk cloth or the yarn may have been sent to merchants elsewhere.

It was the ability to use silk and cotton together and the demand for silk threads of various kinds for elaborate trimmings and embroidery that led to the re-equipping of Bell Busk Mill and Westhouse Mills at Blubberhouses for silk spinning around 1860. With this general trend, more mills were re-equipped for spinning silk in the Halifax area, again for combining with cotton to make a fine cloth, but at a cheaper price. In the Dales, Bell Busk Mill was successful and C A Rickards & Co. exhibited their speciality silk yarns at trade exhibitions around the world. At the same time Samuel Cunliffe Lister developed mechanised ways of combing silk at Low Mill in Addingham, which led to its introduction at High Mill and the building of Burnside Mill, also in Addingham. Velvet made from silk was introduced, and during the Second World War parachute silk was spun and woven in Addingham.

The relatively high price of silk and its attractive appearance led to attempts to copy it when the chemical make-up of fibres became better understood. Rayon was the first manufactured fibre and was originally called 'artificial silk'. Made from wood pulp, it was patented in 1894, first produced commercially in 1910 in the USA, with the name rayon officially adopted by the textile industry in 1924. It was widely used in clothing and home furnishings, and as it is a natural, cellulose-based fibre, its properties are similar to other cellulosic fibres such as cotton or linen. In 1935, at a meeting of the Textile Institute at Wells House Hotel, Ilkley, a representative of Courtaulds, a leading supplier of the yarn, explained how rayon could even be used to make men's suitings. The speaker went on to extol the virtues of rayon, explaining that Britain was falling behind in its use with, for example, Mussolini ordering that all Italian cloth must contain some rayon. In the Dales weaving sheds that survived World War I, rayon was often combined with cotton, but fell out of favour in the 1950s.

Hand and Machine Knitting

In his *Agricultural Survey of the North Riding of Yorkshire,* of 1800, John Tuke noted that agricultural occupations in the western Dales required local people to have some other form of income. This came from knitting and the manufacture of worsted stockings, 'at which they are so expert'. He mentions that hand knitting on needles was so widespread that it was done when people were walking along the roads or in the fields. Today we associate the domestic hand-knitting industry with the northern Dales, but there is still a Stockinger Lane in Addingham and High Mill in the village was spinning yarn for hand knitting in 1812.

Dye houses had been built around Askrigg to meet the needs of knitters in Wensleydale and Swaledale. Gloves, mittens, caps, jerseys and thousands of pairs of stockings were sent to merchants to sell at home and abroad. However, by 1800 fashion had changed and long trousers for men replaced breeches. Knitting continued for another century, but gradually declined.

The demand for yarn by the West Riding worsted manufacturers at that time was so great that spinning on the wheel replaced knitting to a large extent as it was easier and more lucrative. What Tuke didn't foresee was that machine spinning would then sweep away the spinning-wheel so that hand knitting would be important only in the more remote Dales until that, too, was mechanised with the hand needles replaced by hand-operated knitting machines.

The technique used by the hand knitters was different from knitting we know today. To speed up the process a rhythmic motion was adopted as well as the use of a sheath or stick to support one of the needles. This sheath was tucked into a belt and was usually made of wood, often with intricate carving or decoration. Many knitting sheaths and knitted garments, together with some early knitting machines are in the Yorkshire Dales Countryside Museum in Hawes.

Knitters in Hawes

Baines's 1822 Directory noted that in Reeth, 'The staple manufacture of the place is knitted stockings, of which article there is produced in the dales of Swale and Wensley, an amount of at least £40,000 a year, which is bought up principally by the neighbouring hosiers for exportation'. Slater's Directory for 1855 noted that 'The manufactures principally consist of knit hosiery, caps, jackets etc with some other woollen articles'.

Eventually hand-operated knitting machines were introduced, and by 1812 it was estimated that there were 177 framework knitting machines in Yorkshire. This compared with several thousands in Nottinghamshire, Leicestershire and other Midlands areas. The report does not say where in Yorkshire the frames were used, but frames cost about £5. Eventually V-bed and circular machines were used in the Dales to produce larger items such as jacket and waistcoat pieces, which could be produced faster than with hand needles. Carriers made weekly journeys round areas of the Dales, collecting the knitted stockings and other items, whilst at the same time delivering a new lot of wool known as 'bump'.

Although we associate hand knitting with the northern Dales, Arncliffe Show still had categories for hand-knitted stockings and gloves in 1866. There were also special competitions for children knitting the same items. As a source of simple garments and possibly additional income, hand knitting was obviously still important.

Carpet Manufacture

The north-eastern corner of the Yorkshire Dales National Park reaches nearly to Barnard Castle in County Durham. One mill in the Park was part of the carpet-manufacturing industry based on Barnard Castle, where Kidderminster-type carpets were woven in the mid-nineteenth century. In 1847 there were said to be 'extensive carpet manufacturies' in the town, and a nearby spinning mill at Bowes in North Yorkshire supplied them with yarn for carpet weaving. One of the carpet firms in Barnard Castle was Monkhouse & Sons, and by 1855 three carpet-manufacturing firms were listed though there had been five in 1827. Carpet making within the Yorkshire Dales occurred at Haverdale Mill, half of which was used to spin yarn for carpets, which were then woven on handlooms in the mill.

There may have been other carpet weavers active within the Yorkshire Dales. Linton Mill was producing carpet yarn by 1818 and many of the Keighley worsted spinners also spun that type of yarn, though most went to Kidderminster. Another example of carpet manufacturing has been found, this time in Settle. There, John Taylor & Sons were listed as spinners and manufacturers of carpeting in 1841 and Farfield Mill near Sedbergh was used for spinning carpet yarn in the late 1930s. We tend to think of the agricultural labourers and lead miners having nothing more than a tabbed rug on their stone flagged floors, but a contemporary account from 1837 gives a different story of the demand for carpets from skilled workers:

Carpet Manufacture

The art of weaving carpets is carried on to a great extent in England at the present period, as they are now so generally used, not only by the middle, and even the more humble classes; indeed there are few decent journeymen mechanics who have not a carpet of some kind to spread over their apartment on particular occasions; and it is scarcely possible to go into the parlour of a tradesman or shopkeeper without finding the floor carpeted. This general demand does not tend to increase the price of carpets; on the contrary, such is the simple construction of the loom, and the process of weaving carpets is so easily taught, that the supply keeps pace with the demand, and the manufacturers compete with each other in the elegance of their patterns and excellence of their workmanship.

Haverdale Mill from Isles Bridge

Auxiliary Industries

The emphasis in this book is on the power-driven mills that were used for spinning and later weaving. However, the production of yarn or cloth in a mill or factory, as with many other industries, entails the provision of services and materials by a range of auxiliary suppliers. A look at trade directories for particular towns and villages, together with other sources, reveals a wide range of business activities which existed to support both the building and the running of the mills in the early years.

Initially the building of the mill, dam and watercourses needed people to design all the structures and calculate the water power requirements of the line shafting and machinery. Though there were many people with experience of water-powered corn mills, a three-storey cotton mill running 1,000 spindles plus the carding and preparation machines was much more complicated. The mills were larger, as were the waterwheels. Soon this early type of mill, often called the Arkwright model, came to be replaced with even larger mills, sometimes employing steam power and eventually gas lighting. Among the largest waterwheels were two in Westhouse Mill at Blubberhouses, one measuring 39 feet by 10 feet and the other 33 feet by 11 feet.

Very little is known about the architects, if we can use that term, who designed the early mills in the Dales. From the few references available it was often a collaboration between the mill owners and local builders based on a few sketches. A more professional approach was taken by Robert Hargreaves & Co., who had developed some of the first worsted spinning frames and who, with backing from the Birkbecks of Settle, planned a new mill at Linton, near Grassington. They asked masons, carpenters and joiners to meet them at the Hole-in-the-Wall inn at Skipton in April, 1787, where they would be able to examine the plans for the mill. Tenders would presumably then have been prepared for building the mill, which was to be of a 'pretty considerable size'. At the same time, tenders were requested for a three-storey warehouse in Skipton.

The most useful person when a mill was being built was the man who acted as 'clerk of works'. He bought materials and supervised the construction of the mill, its power supply and the machinery. Claytons & Walshman used a builder from Preston when they built Langcliffe Mill. He made trips to look for timber and wood for the waterwheel. Similarly Lister, Orrell & Blackburn leased Eshton Mill in Malhamdale when it was built by Matthew Wilson of Eshton Hall. Wilson's building accounts list a payment to a Mr Wade for surveying and levelling the dam race and many payments to Roger Hartley for various jobs. Birkbeck & Co., who built Yore Mill at Aysgarth, carefully worked out that that they should recoup their capital investment after six months of start-up, but unfortunately knew very little about cotton spinning. Only one of them, Robert Dickinson, an engineer from Lancaster, seemed to have any familiarity with mill construction. They therefore decided to offer William Winstanley, who had cotton-spinning experience, a share in the partnership. He also agreed to take some of the children, who were to work at Yore Mill, to his mill at Walton-le-Dale to learn the necessary skills.

Local builders seem to have been responsible for constructing the early mills and excavating the watercourses. Machinery, however, was more complex and in the early days there were few suppliers. Only one mill in Yorkshire had machinery licensed by Arkwright and his partners. That was Low Mill in Keighley. Knowledge of the basic principles of Arkwright's machines spread rapidly, but initially mill masters had either to buy from one of the few machine-builders or to build on site. The basic metal components could be bought and put together in a wooden frame. This was the preferred method for many of the firms. Most mills had mechanics' shops, well equipped with lathes, anvils and other tools for making machine parts such as spindles. The smiths were kept busy repairing and maintaining the machines and some improved the efficiency and operation of those for which they were responsible.

At least two firms supplied metal and machined parts to the Dales mills. One of these was Butler & Beecroft, of Kirkstall Forge which supplied rods, screws, shafts and sheet iron. Amongst their customers in the Dales were:

1791 – Cockshott & Cunliffe, Low Mill, Addingham – rods, bars, screws
1791 – George Armitstead & Co., Clapham Mill – rods, bars, screws
1792 – Baines & Edmondson, Embsay – rod iron
1793 – Joshua Mason, Gargrave – sundries
1794 – John Merryweather, Embsay – rods and bars
1794 – John Heaton, Rilston Mill – rods and bars
1796 – Hallowell & Co., Bell Busk Mill – iron, square and sheet

The iron rods and bars were turned into the required components by workmen using lathes or blacksmiths using anvils. The second firm, this time in Keighley and run by Richard Hattersley, supplied complex items often made from Kirkstall iron. The rapid growth of the cotton industry in Keighley led to the rise of textile machinery-making firms and then to the development of machine tool manufacturers. This firm, founded by Richard Hattersley, and existing until recent times, produced the essential iron components for making spinning frames. It supplied many of the Dales mills with rollers, spindles, flyers and other ironwork. A few examples are:

1798 – Thomas Parker, Arncliffe Mill – spindles and flyers
1798 – George Armitstead, Clapham Mill – rollers and spindles
1798 – Colbeck, Watson & Co., Westhouse Mill, Blubberhouses
1799 – Ambrose Dean, Town Head Mill, Addingham – doffer teeth
1799 – Thomas Mason, Gargrave – spindles
1800 – Netherwood & Co., Scalegill Mill, Kirkby Malham – fluted rollers
1801 – James Wallace, Rilston Mill – rollers and spindles
1801 – Winstanley, Harrison & Co., Yore Mill, Aysgarth – spindles
1805 – Richard Calvert, Kettlewell Mill – drawing rollers

The handful of machine-making firms in the Dales, all of them small, lasted for only a few years. William Buck, who was a whitesmith, had a forge in Settle on the site of Bridge End Mill and made a range of textile machines including the first flax-spinning frames for Pease & Co. of Darlington in 1796. The first spinning frames for Yore Mill at Aysgarth were made by William Moore from Clapham. Richard Shacklock & Sons made and supplied spindles and flyers from their premises in Embsay. Originally at Sandbanks Mill, they moved to Good Intent Mill about 1855 and renamed it Wessens Bottom Works. Later this became the Crown Spindle Works. The towns would have had small firms which made basic equipment. For instance, Francis Gill made wool combs in Skipton in 1855.

A number of early mills, which could not easily be expanded, were on remote sites, or had been under-capitalised for textile purposes, became bobbin mills or sawmills. Huge numbers of bobbins of various sizes were required for the machines used in the spinning process. Sadly, thousands of these, together with the more expensive shuttles, were burnt in mill yards when the West Yorkshire textile trade declined. Dales mills which made bobbins included Birks Mill near Sedbergh, while Fentiman's Mill in Addingham, Hartlington Mill, Little Mill at West End, Bridge End Mill in Settle, Clapham Mill and Gayle Mill all became sawmills.

There is no evidence of cloth finishing anywhere in the Dales apart from the bleaching of linen. A bleaching ground which had been run by William Demaine at Fewston for 35 years was for sale in 1843 by his widow.

Few records exist about the purchases of raw materials by the firms which occupied the Dales textile mills. The larger firms in the early years of cotton spinning bought from merchants in Lancaster, Liverpool and Manchester, but by 1805 the raw cotton trade had centralised on Liverpool. For instance Robert Walshman, a partner at Langcliffe Mill, went to Lancaster to buy cotton for the new mill in July 1784. When Giles and Robert Redmayne from Giggleswick Mill were bankrupt in 1816 they owed money to John Hurst, a Manchester cotton merchant. Smaller firms were supplied by dealers in their local area. For instance, James Hird was a cotton dealer in the small hamlet of Howgill, north of Sedbergh in 1822.

The large firm of Birkbeck & Co., with their mill at Linton, but warehouse in Skipton, bought wool from the farmers in Lincolnshire and Nottinghamshire around 1800, as did most of the other worsted manufacturers in the area. However, smaller firms, not having the capital or premises to store large quantities of wool, bought from local merchants. In 1855 Robinson Lockwood was a wool stapler in Skipton and John Willis in Gargrave.

Sales are again difficult to be certain about, as few records exist. In the 1780s it is likely that much of the cotton twist went to the Blackburn handloom weavers. However, handloom weavers appeared to be able to weave either cotton or worsted depending on the price they were paid. Unemployed agricultural workers turned to handloom weaving and set up looms where they could. Until the introduction of power-loom weaving, many of the early Dales spinning mills were occupied by firms described as cotton manufacturers in contemporary trade directories, which indicates that they had their yarn woven up locally. In addition, cotton manufacturers who did not have their own spinning mills bought yarn locally. The inference from this is that the spinners were putting out yarn to be woven by local handloom weavers while some men employed other weavers, buying their yarn from the local mill and jenny spinners. Baines' 1822 Directory carefully lists the firms which were solely spinners and those which were also manufacturers. Examples are James Cliffe at Arncliffe, William Cockshott at Malham and John Greenwood & Sons at Airton. Samuel Hartley, also at Airton, was a manufacturer, but did not have a mill. In 1837 Henry Blakey was a shopkeeper and cotton manufacturer in Hellifield which did not have a spinning mill. Most cotton cloth was taken to Manchester 'in the grey' and sold there to merchants for finishing. Similarly in the Washburn valley, where linen weaving continued on handlooms for many years, Isaac Hannam was listed as a linen manufacturer in 1857. When William Potter from High Mill in Addingham was bankrupt in 1826 his assignees were two linen manufacturers in Knaresborough, William Turnbull and Simon Fawcett.

In 1819 an agent advertised in the *Leeds Mercury* that he would take cotton twist (yarn) on commission to sell to the 'most respected manufacturers of cotton piece goods in Lancashire and Yorkshire'.

Richard Hattersley moved to Keighley from Sheffield in 1789 and started a business supplying machine parts to the new textile mills as well as screws and other metal items. It was not unusual in the early years for firms to make their own spinning frames. Many of Hattersley's customers were in the Yorkshire Dales.

SECTION TWO

This section is a gazetteer of all the textile mills which existed in the Yorkshire Dales from 1784 to the present day. A mill is defined here as any building used for processing textile fibres using power-driven machinery. The power was normally water or steam though some horse mills operated nearby in Otley and Skipton, and Fleet's Mill at Long Preston had a windmill to pump water back to the dam to be used again on the mill wheel. Wherever possible the name of the mill has been given, but in should be remembered that if there was a major rebuild, perhaps after a fire or change of ownership, a new name might have been used. For instance, a number of early cotton mills, which could not be expanded, were later used for turning bobbins or as sawmills and those uses have given them their current names. Sometimes, for clarity, the word 'cotton' has been added to differentiate the changed use of a mill or mill site from its earlier corn-grinding use. Where possible the location of the mill has been given, but at times, though the existence of a mill might be well documented, the site was cleared many years ago and nothing has been found. An example here is the cotton mill at Eshton Bridge in Malhamdale. The date when each mill was built or came into use for textile purposes has been given, with reservations when necessary. Similarly the date when textile production ceased has also been given, though that cannot always be precise through lack of evidence. In some cases production stopped temporarily for a number of years because of adverse trading conditions or other factors and then started again and this has been mentioned if it is recorded.

The information has come from a variety of sources, some reliable, some variable. Errors will have occurred and I apologise for these. People with local knowledge about particular mills have been a great help, others I will not have met and I look forward to their comments and corrections. Common problems are the close proximity of two or more mills and not being able to distinguish between them; the movement of firms between different mills; confusion over dates in secondary sources and confusion about ownership, lessees and multiple occupancy. Some new textile mills were built by wealthy people as speculative ventures and then leased. Mills could then be sub-let or part sub-let. This has led to numerous problems as some under-capitalised firms lasted only a year or so or even less. There are examples of firms going bankrupt still owing money to the engineering firms who had made their spinning frames. Names also changed. In recent years most writers have referred to the first mill on Cappleshaw Beck at West End as Aked's Mill, as it was run for most of its life by the Aked family. However, the Akeds did not use that title, but High Mill, and when they advertised it to let in 1841 having rebuilt it after a fire, Croft House Factory. Two areas where errors are easy to make are Embsay, near Skipton and West End in the Washburn valley.

One of the interesting factors regarding the textile mills in the Yorkshire Dales is their size. We expect them to have been small, and most were, as they were early and built at a time when textile machines were simple and required little power. The typical Arkwright-type mill was three storeys high and measured about 60 feet by 30 feet. However, larger mills were built and would not have looked out of place in parts of Bradford. In all 73 mills have been recorded. Where the size has been quoted, for instance in sale notices, the dimensions of each mill at a particular time have been given. Often it was stated that the measurements were 'within the walls', but that may not always have been so. It would have been unwise for vendors to overstate measurements, which could be checked. However, newspaper typesetting from hand-written notes could be responsible for some apparent discrepancies. For example Arncliffe Mill was said to be 60 feet by 28 feet in 1815, but only 48 feet by 28 feet in 1842.

Around Skipton

Most of the mills near Skipton were built for cotton spinning, with many in the villages based on earlier corn mills. Close geographic links with the Lancashire cotton and the West Riding worsted industry meant that the mills which survived after 1850 or so could be used for either purpose. Silk, in the nineteenth century, and man-made fibres in the twentieth, were introduced when overseas competition started the long decline of the UK cotton industry.

Skipton's position on the Leeds and Liverpool Canal made it an important centre with cotton spinning continuing until recent times, though the major expansion was after the late 1860s. A visitor to the area in 1792 observed that:

The country beyond Brouton (Broughton) consists of large wild pasture grounds, twenty fields laid as one, for the cotton trade, with its high pay, has put an end to all thoughts of husbandry; canals and cotton mills are the only thought.

A 1793 trade directory that listed the Skipton spinning mills and also some of the jenny spinning firms in Skipton noted, 'Some other gentlemen have already commenced buildings for the weaving of muslin.' These men were using the yarn from the mule and jenny shops in the town which had carding engines driven by a horse-gin. The combination of hand and machine processes needed to prepare and spin worsted yarn also prompted this description of how Birkbecks operated:

At Skipton there is a large house employed in sorting and combing wool. About 3,000 packs are brought each season from Lincoln, Nottingham, Leicester and Rutland shires. After it is sorted and combed it is spun at the companies' mills, at Linton and Addingham in the neighbourhood and made into stuffs, viz shalloons, callimancoes and all sorts of double goods. The noyles from the combing are used for the Dewsbury and Rochdale trade.

Oats and barley were no longer grown, and Skipton had an annual fair for sheep and cattle from 1779. A Leeds newspaper carried a notice that a bank was to be opened in Skipton in 1802 by Sidgwick, Chippindale, Netherwood & Carr, the leading textile manufacturers in the area, but William Sidgwick withdrew from the partnership in October 1804. However, the bank financed a number of textile enterprises in the area. A necessary addition to the warp yarn produced in the mills around Skipton was weft, some of which, as we have seen, was produced on jennies in horse mills in the town. Andrew Findley and John Stoney, who dissolved their partnership as cotton spinners in Skipton in January 1803 may have been involved in this trade.

Local men involved in the textile trade made use of the Leeds & Liverpool Canal. In 1809 the Craven Navigation Company was set up by Chamberlain, Netherwood & Co. They took a wharf in Leeds and one of their boats sailed from Leeds to Blackburn every day. This would have been of great value in sending local yarn to the weaving firms in and around Blackburn.

The importance of the turnpike road from Skipton through the centre of the 'forest' to Knaresborough was noted a few years after its construction. 'And though scarce a single cart was before seen in the market of Skipton, not less than 200 are weekly attended on that market at present.'

This road, with its easier access to the wheat-growing areas east of the Pennines, brought the demise of most of Craven's corn mills as it was no longer economic to grow oats and barley around every small town or village. In 1793 it was noted that there was a large corn market in Knaresborough which dealers attended. Corn was resold in Skipton and the Dales.

The introduction of textile mills increased wages with both factory workers and farm hands benefiting. In the decade after 1780 wages doubled.

By 1822 Baines' Directory informed its readers,

… the all pervading cotton trade has for some years had a footing here, and a considerable number of webs are produced in the course of the year, in the town and neighbourhood.

It lists three cotton manufacturers who, of course, would have been employing handloom weavers. Another directory in 1828 echoed this fact. 'Several cotton mills are upon the streams in the vicinity; and the spinning and weaving of cotton give employment to a considerable number of persons.'

Before the development of power-loom weaving there were a number of cotton manufacturers in Skipton who would have bought yarn from the spinners in and near the town. Some had weaving shops and many, such as Lee Brown from Snaygill in 1816, sold through the Manchester market. In 1866, another directory noted that '… scattered on the streams in the picturesque parish and neighbourhood are many cotton mills and a few worsted mills'.

One important family in the area were the Dewhursts. Thomas Dewhurst was a farmer and worsted manufacturer. In 1789 he bought Elslack corn mill and converted it to spin cotton, which he sold in Blackburn and Manchester. In 1813 he bought the two mills at Millholme in Embsay. In 1819 John Dewhurst and his brothers leased Scalegill Mill near Kirkby Malham and in 1822 Airton Mill. With the profits from these ventures, they built the original Belle Vue Mill in Skipton in 1828, but for worsted spinning. This burnt down in 1831 and when rebuilt was converted to spin cotton. Other buildings were added and Belle Vue mills became the largest in Skipton.

Draughton Mill

The lease of the ground floor of Draughton Mill was for sale in April 1798 together with a spinning shop and a house. The machinery comprised a cotton picker, two roving billies, a 44 inch card and ten jennies, with between 84 and 112 spindles each. All the machines were said to be in excellent condition and the mill to have a powerful water supply. Robert Pearson from Addingham had to be contacted about the lease. Six months earlier he had been selling some textile machinery at Addingham High Mill and also at his draper's shop.

The mill was still for sale the following year when it was stated that the owner and occupier was William Myers. By then the number of jennies had declined to six.

The mill appears to have been used until 1822 when George Pickup was listed as a cotton spinner in Draughton, but no further references have been found.

Eastby Mill

William Chamberlain was an ironmonger in Skipton and, in the 1780s and 1790s, bought large quantities of iron from Kirkstall Forge. In 1792 he was also in partnership with a man called Wilkinson as cotton carders and spinners in Skipton, probably using a horse mill. As a cotton manufacturer he needed his own supply of yarn and in 1797 he took over Eastby Mill, which had been founded by Goodlad, Hartley & Co. about 1792 when they insured the mill and contents for £1,000. They then leased the mill to Carr & Chippendale until Chamberlain took the lease. Carr & Chippendale had to build their own machinery and started spinning in November 1795. Chamberlain insured his machinery and stock for £600 in 1801 and later that year for £2,200. He sub-let part of the mill and also had buildings in Skipton for spinning weft on mules and jennies, and some handloom weaving. These three properties, together with their contents, he insured for £700, £200 and £100. Chamberlain had a counting house and warehouse near the market place in Skipton as well as another warehouse near the bridge. Both, together with the stock, were insured for £1,000 each. In 1808 he insured a weaving shop, looms and stock in Skipton for £600. This was let to William Booth, Joseph Morvil and other manufacturers.

The original mill at Eastby was described as 'old' in 1804 when a new five-storey mill was built and linked to it. Chamberlain appeared to build much of his own machinery, including mules. Eastby Cotton Mill, which was said to have 'undergone considerable improvement', was to let in February 1813. Another waterwheel had been fitted to use the water a second time in the old mill and the machinery was available at valuation to anyone who took the lease. Wages were said to be low in the neighbourhood and application had to be made to the owner, W Chamberlain. The new mill was just being used as a warehouse at this time and was not filled with machinery until after 1820. However, George Chamberlain and later George & Abraham Chamberlain continued at the mill until 1853.

The mill was for sale in that year and was running 6,984 spindles. There was a 24 hp steam engine and a 32 ft 6" by 3 ft 6" iron and wood wheel. It was said that the mill could accommodate 2,000 more spindles if an extra 10 hp could be provided. The machinery at the time included 29 carding engines and 19 throstles.

In 1857 Towler & Bell occupied the mill and they were followed by Bell & Parkers by 1866, and W & P Parker by 1875, but by 1879 the mill had stopped running. This was a large mill which dominated the village of Eastby for 100 years and provided employment for many of the villagers. It was pulled down around 1900 and only a few traces of the water supply can now be seen.

Primrose Mill, Embsay

This was another occasion when a landowner wished to invest in the new cotton industry, but wanted the mill well away from his house. Building started in 1792 on the estate of Embsay Kirk and in 1797, when the mansion was for sale, the mill was described as 'far out of site of the mansion'. The mill was possibly designed by Allen Edmondson from Churwell on the estate owned by William Baynes. The millwright was Thomas Shepherd of Bradford. Baynes let the mill to John Merryweather, a merchant from Gargrave. His brother was a partner in the large cotton mill at Burley-in-Wharfedale. Merryweather bought rods and bars from Kirkstall Forge in 1792 and 1794, to make into machine parts, but was bankrupt in 1796 and the two-storey mill was for sale the following year. It was said to measure 20 yards by 10½ yards wide with two waterwheels. The bankruptcy hearing was in Manchester.

The Embsay Kirk Estate was for sale in 1810 and included 'a spacious cotton mill at the extremity of the estate'. It was possibly still owned by Baynes as he had traded with Hattersleys in 1807.

This mill was advertised for sale or to rent in March 1815 and was at that time occupied by a Mr Balme for spinning worsted. The mill was three storeys high and measured 66 ft by 32 ft within the walls. The two wheels measured 23 ft and 15 ft. There was a counting house, a making-up room and a blacksmith's shop. The nearby old corn mill could be turned into a house. Primrose Mill was again advertised to let in 1822, when it was said that it could be used for worsted or cotton. The mill was still used for spinning worsted in 1832 and occupied by Balme, though it was offered for sale in 1835. Four worsted spinning frames with 96 spindles each together with some other machines were for sale in 1838 when it was run by Bland & Co.

By 1854 the mill was occupied by Robinson & Wilkinson for spinning cotton, but by 1866 they had started to use part of the mill for making tobacco. Textile use stopped around 1890, when Wilkinson took over the whole mill for making tobacco. About 1917 Primrose Mill was changed into a tannery.

Sandbanks Mill or Embsay Mill, Embsay

This mill produced textiles for one of the longest periods in the Dales. The mill, which is partly used for retailing textiles today, was built by Baynes, Barker, Spencer & Co. about 1792 and insured with the machinery and stock for £1,500 in 1793. George Baynes was the brother of William Baynes at Primrose Mill and was already a cotton spinner in Skipton. Another building alongside the old mill was added by Baynes, Barker & Co., who were described as cotton manufacturers and used this building for hand mules. Other buildings were added. The old mill was leased by Robert Thornton, who also was spinning cotton at Airton and Knaresborough. He failed in 1794 and part of the mill was then taken by Thomas Whitehead, who was also a mule

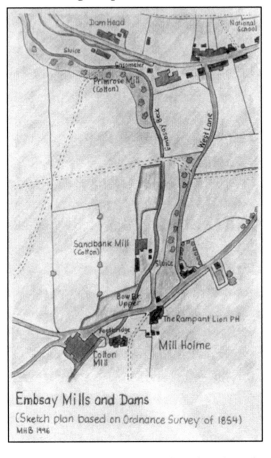

Embsay Mills and Dams
(Sketch plan based on Ordnance Survey of 1854)
MHB 1996

spinner. He failed in 1797 and the mill passed to Edward Whitehead, who bought spindles and flyers from Hattersleys in 1799. In that year Baynes, Spencer & Co. insured the old mill and contents for £700, High Mill and contents for £500 while Edward Whitehead & Co. insured the new mill and contents for £500. Baynes, Spencer & Co. also had a spinning shop in Skipton, presumably a jenny mill, as did Whiteheads.

Sandbanks Mill was advertised for sale or to let in 1805, when it was still being run by Edward Whitehead & Co. The four-storey mill measured 66 ft by 30 ft. The large waterwheel powered 17 mules with 3,000 spindles. Spencer & Co. still owned the mill and bought machine parts for three years from 1804. It was for sale again in 1815, by which time Edward Whitehead had given up the lease. The cotton machinery was available at valuation.

In 1813 this mill and Millholme Mill nearby were taken by Dewhursts. This firm rented several mills before they built the large Belle Vue Mill in Skipton in 1828. Sandbanks Mill was for sale in 1828 when the three-storey mill measured 45 ft by 27 ft. There was also a room at the eastern end where cotton was dressed and together they held preparing machinery and 1,728 mule spindles driven by an 18 ft waterwheel. The firm of J & I Dewhurst was leasing the mill at the time. Isaac Dewhurst insured the mill and machinery in 1831 for £1,350 with the Sun and Manchester Fire Offices.

Sandbanks Mill, together with Millholme Mill, was to let in 1849 together with four cottages and had recently been occupied by William Brigg-Walter. There was a 14 hp wheel and a 12 hp condensing engine to power 2,400 throstle spindles and preparation machinery.

By the 1850s the mill had been taken by Richard Shacklock & Sons, cotton spinners and manufacturers with a sideline in making spindles and flyers for spinning machines. They remained there until at least 1857 and then moved to Good Intent Mill, further up the valley, where they concentrated on spindle making.

In 1864 part of the mill burnt down and the site with the wheel-house, 17 hp steam engine, boiler house, offices, warehouse and four cottages was for sale. It was noted that the river was arched over for 80 yards. By 1866 Sandbanks Mill had been rebuilt and taken by the Embsay Cotton Spinning Company. They built a large weaving shed in the 1870s.

Spinning then gradually reduced at this mill and was replaced by weaving. Like many mills in the Skipton area it operated at times on the 'room and power' system under which small manufacturers operated a few looms and rented floor space and power from the line shafting which ran through the mill. In 1917 J W Midgley & Co., who also ran a mill at Cononley, consolidated their activities on Embsay Mill and renamed the company the Embsay Manufacturing Company. The waterwheel and old steam engine were taken out in 1921 and replaced with two second-hand engines. Various types of cotton cloth were produced, some for export. The mill closed in 1929 at a time of bad trade, but re-opened in 1932 when the weaving of rayon was introduced. Only half the space was used in the mill and about 1938 it was sold to Sterling Silks, a branch of British Celanese Ltd. Mains electricity was brought in to power new looms which had individual electric motors. During the war it was used as an Admiralty store, but re-equipped with new looms about 1946. British Celanese became incorporated into Courtaulds, which was the last firm to produce textiles at the mill. Czech air-jet looms were introduced in the 1960s, but were then eventually replaced with wider looms from the redundant Skelmersdale plant. The larger of the mill dams was filled in when extensions were added to the rear of the mill in 1978/9. Courtaulds were at this time the largest textile firm in the world and production rose for a while. However, despite using the latest weaving machines, production stopped in 1990. The last items produced were head shawls for Saudi Arabia.

Millholme Mill or Millholme Shed, Embsay

It is not clear when this mill was built, but it was occupied by Dewhursts by 1813 when they also leased Sandbanks Mill. They had to insure the mill for £500. When Sandbanks Mill was for sale in May 1828, another mill, presumably Millholme Mill, was also offered for sale. This three-storey mill also measured 45 feet by 27 feet, but had an additional three-storey annexe measuring 52 feet by 19 feet, which held the joiners' and mechanics' shops, a packing room and two pairs of mules with 864 spindles. Altogether the two mills ran 4,332 mule spindles, but it was suggested that they would also hold 100 pairs of looms. This mill had a 20 ft wheel and was also tenanted by J & I Dewhurst.

By the 1850s Millholme Mill had been taken by William Bland for spinning cotton and he was still there in June 1857 when the mill was for sale. A later tenant was Thomas Wilkinson, who was bankrupt by 1863. By 1870 Jonathon Northrop & Co. were spinning and weaving cotton and worsted at the mill, but they were also bankrupt in 1871, though they continued at the mill. In 1875 a new partnership, Northrop, Ward & Hallam, described as stuff manufacturers, started at the mill. In 1882 Isaac Northrop & Co. were merchants in Bradford as well as stuff and cloth manufacturers at Millholme. Northrop started using electric light in this mill in 1884. The weaving shed was to let in 1886 together with 12 new cottages. It was occupied by Hallam & Ward with 120 looms for weaving coatings and cashmere cloth though it would hold 400 looms. This mill closed about 1900 and was demolished.

Good Intent Mill later the Crown Spindle Works, Embsay

Evidence relating to this mill is confusing, but it is likely that a second mill was built on a new site slightly downstream from the original mill because of a dispute over the water supply. The first mill may have been built about 1800 and occupied in 1807 by Samuel Worrel. Certainly early maps show a building and millponds to supply the water for the wheel. However, the water supply was probably very limited as Whitfield Syke Mill further up the valley only had a 3 hp wheel in 1830 and would have controlled the supply to Good Intent Mill. For many years this mill was run by the Bramley family. In 1819 John Bramley bought new iron shafting from Hattersleys in Keighley. This indicates the building of the new mill. A stream called Wessens Beck was diverted to fill two new dams on the hillside to the north of the mill and water was brought onto the wheel in the new mill through two iron launders.

Thomas Bramley & Sons occupied the mill as cotton spinners and manufacturers and sold their pieces from a room at 34 Cannon Street in Manchester in 1816. All the buildings, machinery and stock were insured for £1,100 in 1820 which increased to £1,600 in 1833. Some of the shafting in the mill had been bought from Hattersleys in Keighley. By this time

John Bramley had taken over and handloom weaving had been dropped. Shortly after, a single-storey shed was added at Good Intent Mill and it was offered to let in 1839. The original three-storey section measured 67 ft by 27 ft and had a 24 ft wheel generating about 9 hp and also a 12 hp steam engine. The new shed measured 57 ft by 39 ft, but was still empty. John Bramley, the owner, lived in a house nearby and mill workers occupied six cottages. Eight acres of land was also available.

Mrs Bramley advertised the mill for sale in 1844, which suggests that John Bramley had died. The spinning mill was used for mule spinning with one pair on the second floor and three taking up the whole of the third floor. The new shed was just used as a warehouse. Any purchaser of the mill could take the machinery at valuation.

In 1847 Good Intent Mill and the cotton machinery including four throstles with 204 spindles each, were leased to John Pickles and John Holgate, formerly of Burnley by John Maquis of Embsay. In April 1850 Thomas Lister, from West End, moved his machinery from there to start mule spinning at Good Intent Mill with a lease from John Maquis. However, the second of two mysterious fires in November that year destroyed the mill and his machinery. By 1855 Richard Shacklock had moved here from Millholme to expand his spindle-making business. Local legend has it that one of his forges, bought secondhand from Manchester, had been used to make bayonets for the army at the time of the Crimean War.

Whitfield Syke Mill, Embsay

According to the replies given to the Factories Enquiries Commissioners in 1833, this mill was built in 1795 or 1796 and sited on Whitfield Syke spring. Hammond & Tattersall, who ran the mill, insured the mill and contents for £650 in 1800 and were buying spindles from Hattersleys in 1801. The partnership between John Hammond and Thomas Tattersall of Embsay and Skipton was dissolved in November 1809 and their mill was for sale as well as the lease of a mule shop in Skipton. Whitfield Syke Mill was then three storeys high and measured 46 ft by 28 ft with an 18 ft by

3ft waterwheel. Alongside the mill were five cottages. They had been running six mules with 1,316 spindles and had a well-equipped workshop. At the premises they leased in Newmarket Street in Skipton, they had a further four mules with 854 spindles. John Hammond at the time was 74 and two years earlier had married his cousin Miss Birkbeck, who was then 34.

John Hammond may then have taken William Oldridge as a partner, but this partnership was dissolved in June 1811 with Oldridge paying all the debts. They had been spinning cotton weft both in Skipton and at Embsay. Hammond had borrowed money from Greenwood & Whitaker of Greenholme Mill in Burley-in-Wharfedale, but could not repay the mortgage so Greenwood & Whitaker took over the mill for a few years with William Oldridge as manager. They insured the four-storey mill in 1817 together with six cottages with William Oldridge and others as tenants. William Oldridge was still there in 1822 and was also a cotton manufacturer. With the development of power-loom weaving, Oldridge had given up weaving on handlooms by 1828. In 1833 the mill had a 3 hp wheel and employed twenty-one people, although the mule spinners also employed their own children as piecers. Oldridge was using mules for spinning weft. There appeared to be a constant shortage of water with the wheel giving only 3 hp and the mill frequently running short time.

The mill was for sale in 1838 and the sale notice gave details of two mills on the site. Lower Mill had three working rooms with cotton preparing machinery and 2,044 mule spindles made by Sleddon. This was powered with a nearly new 30 ft wheel. Higher Mill had an 18 ft wheel to drive the cotton blower and willeys and was probably the old mill described above. The property was said to be 'very desirable for any person wishful to enter the cotton business'. In 1857 the mill may have been occupied by John Halliday.

Steam power was added and also a gas plant for lighting. Textile production stopped about 1875 and at the turn of the century the buildings were used as a 'health resort'. The mill was pulled down when Embsay Reservoir was built.

Rilston Mill

The old corn mill, which had served Rilston and Hetton, was owned by the Duke of Devonshire. Richard Waddilove started to convert it for cotton spinning in April 1792. He didn't want to pay the high rent and pulled out to become a partner at the new Hebden Mill and also had an interest in Grassington Low Mill. Robert Bradley took over, but ran into trouble with local landowners as carts carrying materials to the mill were destroying the lanes to the mill. Bradley passed the lease to John Heaton from Horwich, near Bolton in Lancashire, who bought rods and bar iron from Kirkstall Forge in 1794. Bradley wanted a larger mill and put a proposal to the Duke for him to build a larger mill costing £600 or take some land in exchange. The mill was to be four storeys and to measure 75 ft by 30 ft. After the mill was built, Bradley leased it to James Wallace, but he ran into problems and in December 1803 his machinery at Rilston mill was advertised for sale. There were three 30-inch cards, three 204-spindle mules, a throstle with 108 spindles and another with 72 as well as 11 pairs of looms for weaving velveteens. What was unusual, was that with mules and throstles, Wallace was able to spin both weft and warp under one roof and also have it woven into cloth on his looms on the premises. Apparently the machinery was not in good condition and only the mules were sold. The mill was not used again and was demolished in 1826. Today the remains of one of the walls can just be seen alongside the stream.

Hetton Mill

The only references found to this mill are newspaper sale notices in March 1795 and April 1798. The mill was a new building over 24 ft long and was well supplied with water which drove the beater and carding engine. The weft spinning was on jennies. Each of the six jennies had 100 spindles. Included in the sale was a stove, pipes, a press and weights. Application had to be made to the owner Joseph Ellis in Hetton and the mill was said to be in Manheads Close.

Threaplands Mill

Benjamin Shiers, a grazier and cotton spinner, insured this small cotton mill and contents for £500 in 1800. He then bought machine parts including rollers from Hattersleys for three years from 1800. Shiers was still running the mill in 1812, but it was then leased by a Mr Whitaker. However, the mill was for sale in 1818 when details could be obtained from Thomas Shiers of Flasby, James Dewhurst of Skipton or Benjamin Shiers of Wilmot Street in Manchester. No further details have been found.

Marton Mill

John Bond, a publican in Marton in Craven, ran both a small spinning mill for producing warps and a jenny shop nearby for producing weft. He insured both premises together with his machinery and stock for £300 in 1801 and continued until at least 1809, when his wife died. He had also been an agent for Greengate Mill in Keighley, by taking yarn, which came on the Leeds & Liverpool Canal, and then giving it out to local handloom weavers.

Airebank Mill, Gargrave

This mill, appropriately on the river Aire, was built in 1791 by Thomas Mason senior. He died in 1810 and his son, also Thomas, continued spinning cotton at Airebank Mill or part of it until about 1857. The mill, spinning machinery and stock were insured for £2,000 in 1823. However, the installation of the new cotton power-looms in 1826 at a time of trade depression brought opposition from Lancashire handloom weavers. About 8.00 o'clock in the evening of the 27th April 1826, about 200 of the group of rioters who previously in the day had been chased away from Low Mill at Addingham, approached Airebank Mill. Thomas Mason went to meet them and offered financial help if they did not attack his mill. They refused and destroyed 25 newly-installed power-looms and other machinery within about 15 minutes. Overall it was estimated that at the same time nearly 1,000 looms were destroyed over the border in Lancashire. Though Thomas Mason was compensated for his loss with a grant of £350 by the local authority, the Hundred or Wapentake of Staincliffe and Ewcross, power-loom weaving did not start again on this site for some years. Mason insured the mill, machinery and stock for £2,000 in 1831 and in 1833 the mill had a 20 hp wheel. The mill worked the usual 12-hour day and employed 33 people.

At some point the mill was enlarged and part of the mill was taken for worsted spinning. Joseph Smith ran this section from about 1835 until 1842, when his machinery was for sale. This included three combing machines, 30 three and four pitch combs with pots and 18 spinning frames with 96 and 100 spindles each. He also had warp and weft yarn so was also probably a worsted manufacturer. The furniture in his house was also sold.

In 1845 the mill, or part of it, was to let to cotton or worsted spinners, though it had been used for spinning worsted. A 20 hp steam engine had been added to supplement the 16 hp wheel. In addition there was a mechanics' shop, three cottages, outbuildings, a house and garden. This mill was said to be 29 yards long and George Smith or John Rayner would supply further details.

Thomas Mason continued as a cotton spinner and manufacturer until about 1857, but Christopher Bracewell from Earby took part of the mill by 1847 and then the whole of the mill. He was also a cotton manufacturer at the time. Christopher Bracewell & Brothers ran Waterloo Mill in Clitheroe and Victoria Mill in Earby and continued cotton spinning at Airebank for many years. The Bracewells were tenants as the mill was owned by the Wilsons from Eshton Hall. Later Bracewell Brothers ran Butts and Wellhouse Mills in Barnoldswick, a weaving shed in Burnley, collieries at Ingleton, flour mills, quarries and many farms. There was a serious fire at Airebank Mill in 1865 with £20,000 worth of damage and another in January 1874 when £60,000 worth of damage occurred. Until he died in 1891, Airebank Mill and another mill in Earby were run by Henry Bracewell.

Later a much larger mill was built on the site for Sir M A Wilson of Eshton Hall. It was three storeys high, ten bays wide and twenty-six bays long. Whittle & Brindle leased the mill in 1912 when there was another fire which destroyed this building and their entire stock of cotton. The mill was not insured and was not rebuilt.

Johnson & Johnson, a company specialising in medical supplies, had been weaving cloth in Earby, but took the site in 1932 and built a new mill for the production of wound dressings in 1933. They also moved some of their operations to Gargrave from Slough. The site has been expanded, is now occupied by Systagenix Wound Management, and is used it for preparing fibre for wound management systems as well as research and development.

Low Mill or Goffa Mill, Gargrave

Construction of Low Mill started about 1797 and the next year Betty Hudson ordered spindles and rollers from Hattersleys of Keighley for some new spinning frames. Two years later she insured the mill and contents for £1,500. Betty Hudson, probably a wealthy widow, had built Damside Mill in Keighley and her daughter married Thomas Parker, who had been the landlord of The Buck and then the Devonshire Arms in Keighley. Parker built Arncliffe Mill and his sons ran various cotton-spinning mills in the Dales. Low Mill was run by Betty Hudson's grandson, James Parker who, until 1804, had Samuel Gill from Grassington Low Mill as a partner. James Parker & Co. insured the mill and contents for £1,800 in 1810, when it was noted that the mill was under four storeys.

In 1811 James Parker and his partner at Hebden Mill, William Hepworth, were bankrupt so Low Mill was put up for sale. The three-storey mill measured 74 ft by 29 ft on the inside and had a 'most powerful' waterwheel. They were running 14 water twist frames with 48 spindles each, which must have been old, and one throstle with 148 spindles. There was a house for a manager or owner and twelve cottages. It was added that 'In the village of Gargrave, children and proper mechanics are in constant supply, at very moderate wages'. It was also pointed out that the mill was near to the Leeds and Liverpool Canal. James Parker also had to sell some land he owned at Bank Newton near the canal.

In 1838 a worsted mill with a steam engine was listed in Gargrave and in April 1842 a worsted mill was advertised to let. This was probably Low Mill. The rooms in the three-storey mill measured 20 yards by 13 yards and were 10 ft high. The 15 ft wide wheel had a 13 ft fall to it and the mill was a few hundred yards from the Leeds & Liverpool canal. Machinery in the mill included a set of 'very good combing machines', 19 spinning frames with 96 spindles each and the usual mechanics' tools. There was also 30 acres of land available.

Worsted spinning may have stopped by 1853 as there is no mention of this mill in a Trade Directory for that year. By 1911 it was occupied by the Meridian Lighting Company. The later name of Goffa Mill came from its use by the Gofar Tyre and Rubber Company.

High Mill, Gargrave

Joseph Mason bought the corn mill on the site and started building this mill in 1791. In 1792 he insured the mill and his house, with all their contents, for £2,000, but he also had a warehouse on the canal. He soon handed over the running of the mill to his nephew, also Joseph. Another nephew, Thomas, ran Airebank Mill. Machine parts were bought from Kirkstall Forge in the 1790s so possibly they built some of their own machinery. Joseph Mason the younger continued spinning cotton at this mill for many years. In 1818 his mill and contents were insured for £1,400 though by 1857 he was also described as a farmer. In 1853 Thomas Johnson was listed as a cotton spinner and manufacturer at High Mill. Cotton spinning may have stopped in the 1860s.

Today, though the building has been turned into flats, the industrial origins are very clear to see.

Bell Busk Mill, Coniston Cold

Peter Garforth Junior and Thomas Hallowell had used Carleton Old Hall as a spinning shop before they built Bell Busk Mill in 1794. This was a large five-storey mill insured for £1,700 in 1794, and by 1797 £2,500 worth of machinery and stock had been taken into the mill. Some of the machinery was made from iron, rods and screws bought from Kirkstall Forge. Garforth had interests in other cotton mills at Sedbergh, Skipton and Bingley so the mill was leased to Thomas Hallowell & Co. A small steam engine was added by 1816 and J B Garforth took over his father's interest. In that year the insurance value of the mill, machinery and stock was £5,000, which increased to £7,300 by 1818. In 1833 Bell Busk Mill was being used to spin 40s quality cotton yarn on mules. Power came from a 16 hp wheel and the 6 hp steam engine with 107 people employed at the mill. In his replies to the Factories Enquiry Commissioners, James

Garforth was one of the few mill owners who felt that a small reduction in working hours would not harm the employer.

J B Garforth was leasing the mill to Peter Watson in 1837, and in 1841 the machinery at this mill was for sale. It included 38 carding engines, other preparation machinery and 17 pairs of mules with over 3,000 spindles. It may then have been leased by William Slingsby, and certainly by 1857 the mill was being run by William & John Slingsby who, by coincidence, also had a large mill at Carleton.

Bell Busk Mill was advertised to let in 1861. The mill was powered by an 18 hp wheel and a 34 hp steam engine and had gas lighting. The five-storey 130 ft by 28 ft mill held 10,766 spindles and could be used for cotton or paper. The new lease started on the 1st of May, 1862. It was taken by C A Rickards who changed it from cotton spinning to producing silk thread for hand and machine sewing, button-hole twists, knitting, embroidery and weaving. By the end of the century much of their output was exported and 1897 the company had become part of the English Sewing Cotton Company. To help promote the firm's home and export trade, a range of silk products was shown at a number of exhibitions. These included the Leeds Industrial Exhibition in 1868, the Vienna Universal

C A Rickards

Exhibition 1873, the Paris Exhibition in 1877, the Melbourne Exhibition of 1881, the International Exhibition in New Zealand in 1882, the Amsterdam Exhibition in 1883 and, nearer to home, the Saltaire Exhibition in 1887. Various medals were won including a gold medal in New Zealand for sewing silks.

In 1901 production was transferred to Low Mill in Skipton and there was concern in the village about the loss of jobs. November 1908 saw the boiler, beam engine, shafting, pipes and gas-making plant being sold and the mill was left empty, eventually being demolished.

Eshton Bridge Mill, Eshton

Unlike most of the other mills in Malhamdale, no trace of this mill has been found. It appears to have been built as a speculative venture by Matthew Wilson of Eshton Hall who insured the mill and contents for £1,000 in 1797. Some of his notes relating to the building of the mill remain and he may have employed help from John and Roger Hartley, who had set up Scalegill Mill, but were bankrupt in 1792. Included in Matthew Wilson's notes are details of payments for an axletree for the wheel and 57½ sheets of glass for the windows. The mill was advertised for sale in 1798 and was said to be on the north side of Eshton Bridge, but it has not been found on any map. The machinery included the usual cards and drawing frames with the spinning machinery consisting of jennies for weft. The lease appeared to have started in December 1797, but the firm of John Orrell, Cornelius Lister and John Blackburn who had taken it, was bankrupt after trading for a year.

Airton Mill

To be precise this should really be Airton Mills as two mills were built on the river at different times and the view from the river footpath indicates the differences. The old corn mill was for sale in 1785 and was bought by William Alcock, a banker from Skipton, who no doubt was well aware that these old mills made excellent sites for the new cotton mills. He sold the property to the miller, John Hartley, his mother-in-law, Margaret Williams and John Brown in 1787. The next year they added the three-storey cotton mill, which was taken by Robert Thornton who had been a partner at Castle Mill in Knaresborough. This first mill was offered for sale in 1795 when it held six spinning frames with 48 spindles each as well as all the preparation machinery and 'necessary articles for carrying on the trade of cotton spinning'. In 1797 the mill was insured for £600 with the millwork and machinery for a further £400. Mrs Williams's son, who lived in Kent, bought out the other partners and after Thornton's bankruptcy leased the mill to William Ellis who had interests in mills in

Keighley and elsewhere. This was in 1803. Ellis had access to capital and enlarged the mill while Williams enhanced the water supply. In 1807 William Ellis transferred the lease to Lister Ellis and John Greenwood. They insured their millwork, machinery and stock for £1,500 in 1808. John Greenwood was probably running the mill in 1817, when he insured his machinery and stock, but not the mill, for £1,300.

Airton Mill

In 1819 John Greenwood and his partners were forced to put up all their property for sale by the High Court of Chancery. At the time they owned or leased mills at Burley-in-Wharfedale, Birstwith, Bingley, Keighley and Airton. All were used for cotton spinning. Also for sale was Swarcliffe Hall, Greenwood's country house. This temporary setback to John Greenwood may have happened because of the debts his partner, William Ellis, incurred at Westhouse Mill at Blubberhouses in 1816, before the days of limited liability. William Ellis eventually retired to Croft Head in Cumberland.

The original mill at Airton measured 72 ft by 31 ft at this time and had two wheels, 12 ft by 3 ft and 16 ft by 6 ft. The 17 spinning frames held 1,632 spindles.

In 1824 the assignees of John Williams advertised the mill for sale though it was already leased by John & Isaac Dewhurst from Skipton at a rent of £113 a year. The following year Dewhursts, together with Christopher Bracewell of Thornton in Craven, bought the lease and in 1834 acquired the freehold. Two years later they started to build the new, larger mill, complete with a gas plant and steam engine. The chimney for the boilers was said to be 85 ft high and the new waterwheel 25 ft by 20 ft. Dewhursts continued to run the mill in conjunction with their Skipton mills until just after 1900, trading as the Airton Mill Company from 1889 and as part of the English Sewing Cotton Company from 1898. Later it was taken by an engineering company and, during the Second World War, by Reckitt & Coleman from Hull to manufacture disinfectant. A spell housing a poultry business followed until both mills were turned into the attractive apartments we see today.

Scalegill Mill, Kirkby Malham

If you walk downstream from Malham, the large dam and goit, and the first view of Scalegill Mill, very clearly show its industrial past. This mill was built in 1791 by William Serjeantson, a local landowner. The first tenant was Roger Hartley, the brother of John Hartley of Airton Mill, and he insured the mill and contents for £800 in 1792, but was bankrupt the following year and assigned his machinery and household goods to William and John Birkbeck, and John Peat, all of Settle. The mill may have remained empty for a while until it was advertised to let in 1795. There was no machinery, but the mill was said to be in a very desirable situation and wages in the area were low. One of the people who could give details of the mill was Christopher Netherwood of Skipton and he took a 15-year lease from Serjeantson, then insuring the mill and contents for £850 in 1804. There was also a separate warehouse which he insured for £250.

Scalegill Mill, Kirkby Malham

Netherwood & Co. bought fluted rollers for the machinery from Hattersleys in 1800, but then took various partners or leased the mill. In 1805 it was run by Netherwood & Corlas, by 1806 Corlas & Co. and by 1807 Bolton & Corlas. After a gap in 1809 the mill was leased to Joseph Mason the following year. Christopher Netherwood & Sons insured the mill, and contents in the mill and a nearby warehouse, for £1,100 in 1818 when they were running the mill themselves. John Dewhurst & Co. from Skipton bought the lease of the mill in 1819 as an investment and started spinning cotton there by 1821 when they insured all the premises, machinery and stock for £2,800. A separate counting house, warehouse and stable may have been used in Kirkby Malham. All or part of the mill was then leased to the firm of Fryer & Townley for a few years but they were bankrupt in 1828. They had been spinners and power-loom weavers with seven mules, three throstles and ten power looms. The sale details mentioned that 'The taker of the mill, if disposed, might considerably extend the manufacturing department'. Some machinery was sold and by

May 1829 Edward Barrow of Westhouse Mill, near Ingleton, one of the assignees, was selling the rest and would negotiate the lease of the mill. The mill was then run by the Dewhursts until about 1904, when the whole company was reorganized after the death of one of the senior partners. However, part may have been let in the 1880s to Kelly, Hartley & Co.

The mill had been offered to let in 1848 when some useful details were given. The three-storey mill had attics and measured twenty-nine yards by nine yards and the premises included three cottages, a warehouse and stables. As an inducement, it was mentioned that the mill was only four miles from the North Western Railway, which would be opened in 1849. After Dewhursts left, the mill buildings were used for a woodworking business and, in later years, rearing poultry. When I first visited the mill, the water turbines which replaced the waterwheel in 1925 were still in place, but have now gone. The building has been converted into cottages, but the ends of the iron tie bars which were used to strengthen the building, possibly when power-looms were used, are still very visible.

Malham Mill

Anyone who proposed to build a factory by the river which runs between Malham Cove and Malham village would arouse widespread indignation these days. However, in 1785 four partners took the old corn mill at that spot, paying £50 each towards the purchase price of £200 and built a new mill. Richard Brayshaw, who came from Malham, had bought the mill, though he was working as an Excise officer in Liverpool. His partners came from Colne and were William Hartley, a shalloon manufacturer, Robert Hartley, a draper and Robert Moon a woolstapler. The partners agreed to share the cost of building and the initial running costs. In 1786 Brayshaw, Moon & Co. insured the mill for £300 and their utensils and stock for £1,200. Three years later Robert Moon left the partnership and John Brayshaw joined. Both Brayshaws now lived in Malham, but there were arguments when William Hartley withdrew and it could not be agreed how much he should be paid.

Peter Garforth, a cotton spinner from Skipton, and William Marsden from Marsden in Lancashire were asked to arbitrate as the mill was to be divided in 1796. The Brayshaws took part of the mill with eight spinning frames and Hartley four. The following year the Brayshaw section measuring 48 ft by 27 ft was sold to three Cockshutt brothers. Robert Hartley then put up his smaller section of the mill for sale several times as bankruptcy was being forced on him. His section had four spinning frames as well as the usual carding and roving machines and immediate possession was offered. By 1800 the four-storey, 27 ft by 21 ft section was being sold by Hartley's creditors in Colne.

In 1803, Thomas Cockshutt bought some card rollers for his carding engines. On August 21st 1813 the *Leeds Mercury* carried the advertisement shown here for the lease of the mill for twenty-six years. The whole of the four storey mill measured 60 ft by 27 ft and held 12 frames with 48 spindles each. Two of the floors were unoccupied, but could be used for spinning weft. There was a 21 ft fall of water to the wheel from a 'most excellent stream'. The mill may not have been let for in 1822 Baines listed William Cockshott as a cotton spinner and manufacturer in Malham. An attempt to enlarge the mill met with opposition from the owners of the Malham Estate that year. A hidden reason may have been the possibility of mill work forcing up local agricultural wages, but this was not stated.

Leeds Mercury, 21 August 1813

Gisburn, April, 1822

Dear Sir, - My Lord Ribblesdale and the Hon'ble Thomas Lister are averse to the Establishment of a Cotton Mill at Malham ... Altho'it is Possible, if a flourishing trade should take place, a transitory Emolument might be derived from it, yet in the end it would prove a Heavy Incumbrance upon the Landed Interest by the Introduction of a needy population, and a total Change in the Innocent Habits and Morals of the present Generation. The daily school would be deserted for the cotton mill. The Boys and Girls in very early life abandoned to Promiscuous Intercourse, their Minds depraved and their Bodies by excessive labour (14 Hours a day) and intense Heat (the Atmosphere of a Cotton Mill not being less than 90 degrees) so much debilitated and emaciated that few arrive at the Age of Maturity. For this Sacrifice of Human Beings the Cotton Maker may become rich, but should he fail it is needless to point out the dreadful State of the Children and the Landowner. – Malham is now a peaceful, contented and happy village. If this Cotton Mill is enlarged and re-established, in a few years the town will be full of Misery, Vice and Debauchery. – These are the sentiments of My Lord and Mr Lister. I hope they will be in union with those of the Freeholders of Malham. His Lordship has ever been Anxious to promote their Wishes upon all Occasions. Yet he cannot conceal his fears and apprehension that the Evils above stated will inevitably be the consequence. His Lordship can give no Countenance whatever to the Mill's Extension, thinking that its present Capacity is large enough to produce too many of the Calamities which other parts of the Kingdom have so fatally experienced.

I am, Dear Sir, Most Respectfully, Yours

M. Knowles

The opposition to the expansion of the mill may also have led to the cessation of cotton spinning at Malham Mill, perhaps by 1825. By 1850 it was said that:

...to view the cove the visitor must proceed up the village, and turn into the pastures above a ruined cotton mill which by no means adds to the beauty of the scene.

Wharfedale and Littondale

Addingham

Today only Otley, Burley-in-Wharfedale and Addingham have traces of their extensive 19th-century textile industries. However, many other towns and villages further up the valley also had textile mills, some on the Wharfe such as Linton, others on side valleys such as Arncliffe and Hartlington. In addition the earlier hand-based industry had been widespread. Handloom weavers of cotton worked around Barden in 1807 and cotton and worsted weavers were still working in Cray and Buckden in the 1840s. Wool combers were at work in Grassington in 1841 preparing tops for the spinning frames at Linton Mill. James Falshaw, a calico manufacturer from Kettlewell, attended the Manchester market every week with rooms at 34 Cannon Street. Three Falshaw brothers worked as wool combers in Starbotton in 1851, but would soon meet with competition from the new machine combs in the larger mills.

During the nineteenth century Addingham was very much an industrial village, with more mills for its size than any other in the Dales. The capital invested in the mills was used for producing a variety of yarns and fabrics over the years. The first worsted mills in Yorkshire were built here at the end of the eighteenth century and in recent years one of them had new machinery installed for wool scouring, though that has now finished. New mills were built, and additions were made in the late nineteenth and twentieth centuries, when most Dales villages were losing their textile workers to the large towns.

Before the first textile mills were built in 1787, Addingham, as with most of the Dales villages, was occupied by people engaged in the domestic textile trades. Flax dressers and linen weavers worked alongside wool combers and worsted weavers. Spinning for both types of yarn would be done by the women in the village. The movement away from domestic production to mechanisation happened over a number of years with the different processes being speeded up in turn. Addingham played an important part in this from having the first worsted spinning mill in Yorkshire in 1787 to the development of the worsted-combing machine which became widely available in the 1850s. The two events were linked by members of the same family. Similarly advances in the processing of silk led to the establishment of the silk industry in Addingham mills.

By 1818 a number of Addingham men attended the Manchester market to sell their yarn and cloth. These included the firm of Bond & Cockroft and many members of the Cockshott family, who had rooms at 34 Cannon Street in Manchester. Another six were also listed including Ambrose Dean who ran Town Head Mill. In 1822 Addingham was said to be:

... a populous and thriving village, the inhabitants of which are chiefly employed in the manufacture of cotton.

This was repeated in 1828, but by 1834 it was reported that:

The spinning of cotton, and the manufacture of goods from that material is carried on here by four establishments; besides which, the woollen trade is advancing in importance.

In 1855 there were four cotton manufacturers and worsted spinners and manufacturers. At the time of the 1851 Census it was reported that most farms in the area were small and not much corn was grown so the farmers needed a second occupation. Thirteen of them were also wool combers and two were handloom weavers. These occupations would soon disappear.

Low Mill, Addingham

According to an early deed, Low Mill was planned as a cotton mill. The partners, John Cockshott and John Cunliffe, had been assigned land on the Wharfe and bought more from Isaac Robinson. After building a three-storey mill in 1787, they decided to install preparation and spinning frames to spin worsted yarn. This was possibly because it was a bad year for the cotton industry. It is not known who made the machinery, but it would have been adapted from cotton frames. The partners added a warehouse and cottages, and when the machine-spun yarn was introduced to the Bradford market, it was well received.

In June 1793, John Cockshott, who was a cotton manufacturer, and who by then also had a half share in High Mill, was bankrupt. He moved to Tong Park, near Baildon, as a partner with Thomas Halliday at the worsted mill there. Several of his Addingham workmen went with him. Low Mill was then advertised for sale by his former partner John Cunliffe. At that time the mill held two waterwheels and 32 spinning frames. Some seventeen cottages had been completed and another four were being built. There was also a farm and fourteen acres of land. The mill was then bought by Nicholas Cunliffe and Thomas Gill, who insured it and its contents for £2,950 in 1797. Gill stayed only a few years though the partners bought bar, rod and sheet iron from Kirkstall Forge to make additional machinery. Thomas Gill possibly left the partnership in 1801 when the mill was for sale. An increase in the number of spinning frames from 32 to 36 provided 1,824 worsted spindles. The mill was then run by John Cunliffe & Sons until 1811 when it was leased by Messrs Pullan. The advertisement for the lease on 31st December 1810 gave more details. The two wheels now powered 40 spinning frames as well as all the preparation machines. There was a warehouse, workshops for maintaining the mill and machinery, and now 26 cottages. It was said that the mill could be used for spinning worsted, flax or cotton. Pullans continued with worsted

EXTENSIVE WORSTED & COTTON MILLS IN ADDINGHAM.

TO BE LET, FOR A TERM OF YEARS, a Substantially-built MILL, called Low Mill, Four Stories in Height, situate on the River Wharfe, with Two large WATER WHEELS, and commodious WAREHOUSES adjoining the said Mill; and 24 COTTAGES belonging to the same Mill; and about TWENTY ACRES of excellent Meadow and Pasture LAND, near the said Mill.

The Mill has been used with great Advantage for Spinning Worsted Yarn; it has very extensive Power, and is capable of running from Five to Six Thousand Spindles. There never is a Scarcity of Water, and the Wheels cannot be thrown into Back-Water.

N.B. If the Mill be not Let before the 1st July next, it will be offered for Sale by Public Auction.

And also to be Let for a Term of Years,

Another Substantially-built MILL, called High Mill, Three Stories in Height, situate also on the River Wharfe, with a powerful WATER WHEEL belonging to the same Mill.

This Mill has lately been used for Spinning Cotton, and is capable of being employed in Spinning Worsted or Flax.

The Mill's may be viewed on Application to Mr. Trees, of Addingham; and further Particulars may be had by applying to Ellis Cunliffe Lister, Esq. Manningham-House, near Bradford; William Cunliffe, Esq. Farfield, near Addingham; or at the Office of Mr. Crosley, Solicitor, in Bradford.

Bradford, 7th May, 1822.

Leeds Mercury, 6 July 1822

spinning until 1820 with 1,900 spindles, when the machinery was for sale. Another floor had been added to the mill and hand wool-combing was obviously important as there were 250 pairs of combs complete with comb pots and seats. Some years of the lease were left and the mill was advertised to let again in 1822 together with High Mill. John Cunliffe's son Ellis would provide details of the mill which it was claimed could run 5-6,000 spindles. If the mill was not let, it was to be sold. However, it was taken by Jeremiah Horsfall in 1824 on a 20-year lease and re-equipped with cotton machines. While Low Mill was being used for worsted spinning, one of the hand-combers came to the mill to collect his wool, which was weighed out to him together with the soap for washing. He saw the key left in the lock of the warehouse door and made an impression with it in the soap. At home he filed an existing key to the same shape and then went back at night to steal ready-combed tops from the bins. The losses were noticed and the thief was apprehended the next time he broke in.

After leasing Low Mill, Horsfall promptly added a large new spinning mill and weaving shed with power-looms, which prompted an attack on the mill on Wednesday, the 26th April 1826. This had been anticipated following riots in Lancashire, and the book-keeper from the mill had written to William Vavasour of Weston Hall, JP and Deputy Lieutenant of the county, for assistance to repel the expected unemployed weavers from Lancashire. Vavasour wrote to the general in charge of the local militia, and the Otley troop of the Yorkshire Hussars were quartered at the mill. Others stayed at mills in Burley and Otley, until May 9th. During the attack, the entrances to Low Mill were barricaded and soldiers were stationed at the upper windows. The leaders of the rioters asked to be allowed into the mill to destroy the looms. Mr Lawson, the superintendent (manager) refused, but offered the men money to help relieve their poverty. They declined and attacked the mill with stones, breaking many windows. The Hussars fired over the heads of the rioters, but when this did not stop the assault they fired at them. Ellis Cunliffe Lister, a JP, arrived and read the Riot Act at which point the men dispersed. The rioters did not gain access, though some outhouses were ransacked. One rioter was drowned and others, from Keighley, were wounded by gunfire. Four men were caught and two were committed to York Castle.

By the next day, a small body of cavalry from Leeds were stationed at the mill. Ellis Cunliffe Lister went there in the morning when several groups of men approached the mill. They withdrew when they saw the cavalry. However, in the afternoon it was reported that several thousand men in military order could be seen about a mile and a half away. The Dragoon Guards were ordered to attack the nearest group, who ran away, but two men were arrested and tried. One was deemed to be a mute and the other was acquitted as only being there out of curiosity. Eventually the rioters withdrew, but 200 marched through Skipton to Gargrave, where they were approached by Thomas Mason from Airebank Mill who offered them help to relieve their poverty. They refused and destroyed his looms. Most of the men were from the Colne and Laneshaw Bridge area, but had picked up others on the way. In addition to the attack on Low Mill, some new mules destined for the mill from the manufacturer in Cheshire were destroyed on the way on the Tuesday afternoon. The rioters thought they were power-looms.

In a letter in the *Leeds Mercury* on May 6th, it was argued that the reasons for the riot were the extremely low wages paid for handloom weaving coupled with the shortage of work. The writer went on to explain that 'Calicoes, for which 5/- a piece was paid for the weaving 20 years ago, are now woven in some districts, on the confines of Yorkshire, at 10d a piece, and 1/- is the maximum price in Addingham, and in this part of the country'. There appeared to be some sympathy with the plight of the unemployed handloom weavers and other textile workers with the king and aristocracy contributing to their benefit funds. The poverty of the handloom weavers was so well known that slaves in Jamaica sent money to help them.

Jeremiah Horsfall built a school for the mill children where small children were taught daily and those who worked could attend when they finished. As they worked 12 hours a day from 6.00 am until 7.30 pm that must have been difficult. However, they could learn to read and write at the school on a Sunday. The mill, lit by gas, machinery and stock were insured for £4,400 in 1827. By 1839 this had increased to £25,000 with the risk taken equally by the Sun, Norwich Union and Lancashire & Yorkshire Fire Offices.

Horsfall, who lived at Farfield Hall, was bankrupt by 1841 and the large mill and weaving shed he had built on the site were offered to let by Ellis Cunliffe Lister and other assignees. The five-storey mill had two iron waterwheels and was lit with gas. Any tenant was required to take the nearly new cotton machinery at valuation. This included 12,500 mule and throstle spindles as well as 280 power-looms. The rent was said to be very low at £600 per annum.

TO COTTON SPINNERS AND MANU-FACTURERS.—TO BE LET, from Year to Year, or for a long Term of Years, with immediate Possession, at the very low Yearly Rent of £600, all that very extensive Stone-built MILL, Five Stories high, situated on the Banks of the River Wharf, near to the Village of Addingham, lately occupied by Mr. Jeremiah Horsfall, for the Spinning and Manufacturing of Cotton; with Two large Iron Water Wheels of the best Construction, nearly new, of abundant Power, and turned by a never-failing Supply of Water from the Wharf; together with commodious WAREHOUSES and GAS WORKS thereto adjoining and belonging; also a good DWELLING-HOUSE, with Garden and Orchard, and THIRTY-ONE COTTAGES, within a short Distance of the Mill, and about 20 Acres of rich Meadow LAND adjoining.

The Tenant will be required to take the Machinery, which is nearly new, and by first-rate Makers, at a Valuation. It consists of 12,500 Mule and Throstle Spindles, 42 Card Engines, 79 Power Looms, Machinery for preparing, and every requisite and Convenience for carrying on the Spinning and Manufacture of Cotton.

The Mill, which is heated by Steam Pipes, is in excellent repair, and situated within Three Miles of the Leeds and Liverpool Canal; Six Miles from Skipton and Keighley, and Eight Miles from Otley, and on a Line of good Road into Lancashire.

The Premises are in every respect adapted to the carrying on the Cotton Business on an extensive Scale, and a desirable Opportunity is afforded to any Person wishing to engage in such a Concern, as, besides the lowness of the Rent and Assessments, Hands are plentiful and Wages moderate.

Mr. Peter Johnson, of Addingham, will show the Premises, and further Information may be obtained of Ellis Cunliffe Lister, Esq., Manningham House, near Bradford; John Dewhirst, Esq., of Skipton; Mr. John Heatlands, Bingley; or at the Office of

Mr. TOLSON, Solicitor, Bradford.

Bradford, Feb. 2, 1841.

Leeds Mercury, 20 February 1841

William Threlfall and William Seed took the mill in 1842 with a 21-year lease, but were bankrupt by 1851. The mill was owned by members of the Cunliffe-Lister family and for some reason a one-eighth part was for sale in that year. William Threlfall's son John, had taken on the lease of Westhouse Mill at Blubberhouses and Low Mill at West End, but his father's bankruptcy stopped both ventures.

Low Mill was then taken by Samuel Cunliffe Lister, a very successful textile inventor, who by 1851 had developed a combing machine from which he made his first fortune. This patented machine, though expensive, replaced the work of dozens of hand wool-combers and brought an end to their trade within a few years. S C Lister continued cotton spinning at Low Mill, but also further developed his machine comb, this time to comb silk waste. Eventually he was successful and he moved into silk combing and spinning and the making of velvets. By employing talented engineers Lister was able to develop many machines. In 1855, possibly at a time when Lister's energies were being devoted to development work, part of Low Mill was leased to Warburton & Co. for spinning Berlin Wool, which was used for embroidery. Warburton helped Lister with his work in developing the silk comb, but was eventually bought out. Lister went on to develop a power loom for weaving velvet and these were introduced into Low Mill.

In February 1883 the mill dam burst and half the motive power for the mill was lost. The workers were put on short time and could work only the machinery that was run from the power of the steam engine. It was said that the clearing of the river and reconstruction of the dam would cost several thousand pounds.

Low Mill, Addingham

After the First World War Listers diversified into mohair and knitting yarns and in 1926 built an additional three-storey mill which exists today. This mill was not put into use immediately because of bad trading conditions, but in 1932 a partnership was formed with a German company to produce velvets in a new weaving shed with advanced German looms. Silk yarn for this purpose was produced in the new mill. In 1941 the looms were removed to Bradford and the mill was taken by S U Carburettors to make aircraft carburettors as part of the wartime policy of spreading industry to rural areas. Textile production did not stop as parachute silk was produced and after the war, full production started again, but was gradually reduced, ending in 1976. Then the remaining domestic buildings together with the transport shed were converted into modern homes and new houses were built on the site of the older mills and sheds.

Low Mill, Addingham

Today the remains of Low Mill with its ancillary buildings and workers houses provide the site for a pleasant residential community which is a little separate from Addingham itself. The oldest mill premises have gone and been replaced by modern houses. The narrow street of workers' dwellings is still there with the properties modernised and some still overlooking the dam on the river Wharfe. A postscript to the story of Low Mill as the first worsted mill in Yorkshire was the re-equipment of part of the remaining 1926 mill buildings for wool scouring in 1999. Much opposed by people in the expensive new properties, this enterprise lasted until 2004. Now loft living has come to Low Mill with the conversion of this last mill into apartments.

High Mill, Addingham

Henry Lister and John Cockshot, cotton manufacturers in Addingham in 1785, needed to balance their supply of yarn. Warp thread was easily acquired from the new cotton mills in Keighley; they bought £276 from Blakeys, Smith & Watson at Greengate Mill in 1786, but they needed a proportionate amount of weft. This they secured by leasing room at High Mill and installing preparing machinery and jennies, all insured for £700 in the same year. A new mill, 90 ft by 28 ft, was then built alongside by a nine-man partnership. The important partners were the Birkbecks from

Settle and Robert Hargreaves who was a cotton manufacturer. The Birkbecks contributed money and experience gained at other mills such as Yore in Wensleydale, and Hargreaves his skill in developing worsted spinning frames. The partnership agreement between William Birkbeck and Robert Hargreaves was drawn up in 1787. They then moved to Linton Mill. By 1794 corn, worsted and flax were all being processed, with the cotton section run by William Bland. High Mills were being sold as the owner, Richard Smith, had died. John Cockshot was bankrupt and his half was for sale. The jenny mill may have been taken by Robert Pearson, a draper in Addingham. He was selling the cotton machinery with a cotton picker, three cards, four roving billies and 19 spinning jennies in 1797. He also had a quantity of slays so he was also probably a cotton manufacturer. Pearson also ran Draughton Mill. The mills had several occupants during the next few years including William Boothman in 1800. He bought rollers for his spinning frames in that year.

The older part of the mill was to let in 1804. There were several large rooms and warehouses together with four flax-spinning frames. George Scott on the premises dealt with prospective purchasers or they could apply to John Goodman and Samuel Elam of Leeds. The mill continued to be let, but in April 1808 William Holdsworth was bankrupt and all his stock in trade, machinery and household goods were for sale. He had yarn, flax and tow which would have been spun on his seven spinning frames. Three months later the two mills were to let. The flax mill had an 18 ft by 2 ft wheel and the worsted mill an 18 ft by 4½ ft wheel. The fall of nine feet enabled the two wheels to generate 30 hp. Both mills, described as Addingham Mills, were owned by Goodman & Elam. Part of High Mill was advertised to let in 1809 when it had three storeys, 50 ft by 30 ft and a new waterwheel. The flax mill then appears, from the insurance and other records, to have been divided with part turned back into a corn mill, with the worsted mill left empty for a year or so. It was then taken by Baxter & Brigg who were bankrupt at the end of 1812. Their assignees sold their machinery in January 1813. This included the usual stock of comb pots, preparing machinery and five spinning frames. This machinery had been used to spin yarn for knitting stockings for men and women. Later that year the empty premises were advertised to let again by John Smith, who was also a grocer in Addingham.

In 1822 Ellis Cunliffe, who then lived at Manningham in Bradford, advertised the lease of both Low Mill and High Mill, where cotton had been spun in the three-storey mill. The Cunliffe-Lister family owned High Mill by 1818, though it was let to various firms until 1869. For example, William Potter may have been spinning flax there in a small way until 1826 when he was bankrupt. In 1822 High Mill had been taken by Bland, Ellis & Co., who possibly used sections for spinning cotton and worsted yarns. Cotton, however, was soon dropped. The partners prepared the answers to the Factory Enquiry Commissioners questions in 1833. It may have been that by then they only occupied part of the mill as they used only one 8 hp wheel and employed only 21 hands. Though the firm worked the long hours that were normal at the time, they appeared to have had a paternal attitude to their employees. They argued that their workers were satisfied with the hours they worked, they lived well, dressed well, looked well and not one child had died at the mill for ten years.

By 1843 power-looms had been installed in part of the mill. The 50 pairs of six quarter looms together with six spinning frames with 596 spindles were included with the mill when it was advertised to let. The machinery was said to have been made by the best machine makers in the county and was driven by two waterwheels.

William Bland continued spinning worsted until Listers took over in 1869 and re-equipped the mill for silk spinning. Eventually silk weaving was introduced and cloth with a silk warp and cotton weft was produced. Northrop automatic looms were installed between the wars and a water turbine replaced the waterwheel in 1919. Listers continued at High Mill until 1953, when it was taken over by a light engineering firm for some years. It is now flats, though some of the old buildings have been demolished.

Townhead Mill, Addingham

An insurance policy of 1799 provides the first reference to Townhead Mill. In that year Ambrose Dean insured the building and its contents for £400. He also bought some parts for a cotton-cleaning machine called a devil. In 1802, Dean bought additional land for £900, thus enabling him to control Town Beck which flowed past his mill. The water supply was probably inadequate to power his machinery, and in 1803 we find him negotiating with Boulton & Watt in Birmingham for a 6 hp steam engine. Dean was helped in this by his father-in-law John Cockshott, formerly of Low Mill in Addingham who, after his bankruptcy, joined Thomas Halliday at Tong Park Mill in Baildon which already had a Boulton & Watt engine. This new engine was delivered to the canal wharf at Silsden and taken over the moor to Addingham, where Dean had prepared the engine and boiler house.

Dean had ten throstles with 126 spindles each in 1811, but also produced or bought weft, as he was a cotton manufacturer, selling on the Manchester market. He decided to retire in 1820 and started to advertise the lease of the mill together with the 6 hp Boulton & Watt engine which could be worked together with the waterwheel. Anyone who took the mill could also take the machinery. Further details were added to the advertisements in 1824. The mill was three storeys high and measured 40 ft by 24 ft, but also had an attic. A nearby warehouse had the same dimensions as the mill and there was an additional counting house. To widen the appeal the mill was said to be suitable for cotton, worsted, flax, paper, corn or power-loom weaving. Whoever took the mill probably turned it over to spin worsted. Townhead Mill was to let again in 1827, still powered by the 6 hp Boulton & Watt engine. This time application had to be made to John Dean. The whole or part of the mill was then taken by Robinson Brigg who was bankrupt by 1841. His three worsted-combing machines, preparing and spinning frames, together with ten power-looms made by Fox & Bland of Keighley, were all for sale. John Cockroft & Sons, who were running the rest of the mill, became bankrupt three months later. Their machinery was being sold by their assignees and included 70 pairs of 3- and 4-pitch wool combs, 1,716 worsted spindles and 50 pairs of power looms again made by Fox & Bland of Keighley. George Bland of Keighley was one of the assignees so it looks as though poor trading conditions meant that John Cockroft & Sons could not pay for their new looms or their other debts.

On the 30th October 1841 the *Leeds Mercury* reported that:

Trade continues to be in a wretchedly depressed state both in Yorkshire and Lancashire; and there is the prospect of a winter of most severe suffering, if not of terror.

Townhead Mill was taken by Thomas Beck from about 1845. In 1875 John Hartley and Robinson Hargreaves, who were worsted manufacturers in Bradford, ran the mill, presumably for worsted spinning and weaving.

After the First World War William Watson took Townhead Mill for weaving rayon for home and foreign markets and weaving continued, subject to trading conditions, until 1971 when the looms were taken out. Several small enterprises now occupy the old weaving shed.

Fentiman's Mill or Saw Mill, Addingham

Known in recent years as the Saw Mill and now converted for residential use, this mill has the rare indication of the date it was built and the initials of the owner chiselled into a stone high on the side. Anthony Fentiman built the mill in 1802 following some years' experience in the cotton industry in Skipton and possibly also at Beamsley Mill. In 1799 three mules were left in Skipton for him which might have been intended for the new mill. This seems likely as the mill was being used to spin weft in 1804. Fentiman, who lived at the manor house, was also a calico manufacturer and by 1816 had premises at in Cannon Street, Manchester. His two sons, John and William, had joined him at the mill by 1822, but by 1825 the building was to let. It had been used for cotton spinning and had a spacious warehouse together with a house and land. It may not have been taken, for Anthony Fentiman was still there in 1828, and it was offered for sale again in March 1829, together with a pew at the Parish Church. The mill measured 52 ft by 27 ft and was offered with a manor house and three cottages, but there were no takers as John Fentiman still occupied it in 1834 as a cotton spinner and manufacturer.

Fentiman's Mill or Saw Mill, Addingham

A few years later the mill was bought by Thomas Lister Cunliffe. John Booth was renting the mill from him in 1838, but John Fentiman still had an interest in 1850. By then it may have been converted to spin worsted. From about 1854 it was occupied by Timothy Brear, who was a spindle maker, but within a year or so it was converted to a sawmill, hence its present name. The Brear family continued preparing wood products at the mill until recently.

Burnside Mill, Addingham

This mill, built in 1886, is only a few yards from the main street in Addingham and is now flats. It was built alongside Town Beck, not for water power, but for condensing water for the steam engine and was built by one of the sons of William Watson, the manager at Low Mill. Initially it was used for silk spinning, but later was incorporated into the Lister group. Production stopped in 1948 and the machinery was moved to one of Lister's mills in Barrow-in-Furness.

Burnside Mill, Addingham

Wolseley Shed, Addingham

This was a single-storey shed built for weaving worsted by Sam Walton from Silsden in 1880. Walton had offices at Charles Street in Bradford. After the First World War it was taken by Bolton, Emmott, Cockroft & Co. who started weaving rayon and mixed fabrics for home and foreign markets. A heavy snowstorm in early 1933 brought down part of the roof of the weaving shed and work stopped for some time. Production continued through the Second World War, but ended in 1959. Houses now occupy the site.

Wolseley Shed, Addingham

Barcroft Shed, Addingham

A half-completed mill at Southfield was equipped with looms after the First World War, renamed Barcroft Shed and run by a man called Adams. He was weaving artificial silk like other Addingham weavers at the time. After 1945 the mill was used for knitting nylon fabric, but closed in 1959.

Beamsley Mill

This mill, which can be seen today, was one of many corn mills converted internally to spin cotton in the early 1800s. However, the venture was not successful in the long run and the building has been little altered. Early in 1818 it was advertised to let after being used for cotton spinning and it was said to be near the turnpike road from Skipton to Knaresborough. It was for sale again in 1821 and then said to be suitable for cotton or worsted spinning or corn grinding. The mill measured 27 ft by 27 ft and held a 26 ft wheel. Textile production probably stopped at that point. An interesting footnote is that in 1980 the breast shot wheel was being repaired as it provided power for a craftsman woodworker who specialised in the manufacture and restoration of church furniture. At that time it was said to be 28 ft in diameter.

Beamsley Mill

Leeds Mercury, 3 January 1818

BEAMSLEY MILL.
To be LET, and Entered upon Immediately,

ALL that MILL, and Premises thereto belonging, formerly used as a CORN MILL, and of late Years as a COTTON MILL, situate at Beamsley, near Bolton - Bridge, Six Miles from Skipton.

It is particularly well calculated for either purpose, being supplied with a never-failing Stream of Water, and is near the Turnpike Road from Skipton to Knaresbrough.

Wm. Winterburn, of Bolton-Bridge, will show the Premises, and for further Particulars apply to Mr. Preston, at Skipton.

Hartlington Mill, near Burnsall

The old corn mill and new cotton mill were advertised for sale in May 1789 together with a warehouse and were in the possession of William Myers who was a cotton manufacturer. It was added that 'the premises are well adapted for being converted to any of the branches of machine spinning, and stand upon the banks of a very powerful rivulet'. The mill was then taken by James Brown, a grocer, Edward Moorhouse, a grazier, and Richard Atkinson, a stonemason, all of Skipton. James Brown & Co. insured their mill and machinery for £650 in 1800. There was also a counting house, hanking room and storeroom adjoining.

Hartlington Mill was to let in 1812 and was said to be on the high road from Grassington to Skipton. The three-storey mill had two upper rooms measuring 43 ft 6 inches by 27 ft, but only 16 ft in the lower room as it was built into the hillside. There was also a 33 ft by 13 ft warehouse adjoining with a counting house and other rooms underneath. The machinery was also available to whoever wished to lease the mill and included nine cards and eight spinning frames each with 48 spindles. The lease had expired and so the mill was being let for a further term. James Brown of Skipton would give information about the machinery so was still involved with the mill. The advertisement said that 'The River Wharfe affords a plentiful supply of water', though anyone visiting the mill would have found that Hartlington Mill was not on the Wharfe, but on a side stream.

An original notice for the remaining years of the lease hangs in the bar of the Red Lion at Burnsall. Nine years of the lease were left on 14th March 1814 and the sale was to be on the 5th January 1815 at the public house. The lease was for sale again in 1817 and the cotton machinery in the mill was still available. This time the nearness to Skipton and the Leeds and Liverpool Canal were stressed. The owner was Thomas Bland of Hartlington and it was suggested that the mill could be used for spinning worsted, flax or cotton or even making paper. Land and cottages were also for sale and the purchaser could buy the machinery in the mill.

About 1830 the mill was taken and occupied for many years by Jeremiah Ambler who was a worsted spinner with a mill in Baildon near the Bradford Canal. In 1835 fifty-two people worked there, but only eight were over twenty-one. The use of power-looms in the Dales textile mills appears to have extended to Hartlington as two power-loom weavers were listed in 1841. Hand combing was still well established with many of the combers living in Appletreewick. The overlooker at the mill was Thomas Foullan. In 1848 the mill was to let with the top room extended to 66 ft. The mill dam may have been raised at the same time. The mill had a wheel 18 ft by 6 ft and the worsted machinery could be taken at valuation. It is not clear when textile production stopped at this mill, but

Leeds Mercury,
25 January 1817

the parish records for Burnsall show that Robert Rennard from Bradford was the mill manager in 1876. Later the premises became a sawmill. Today the mill looks well preserved, having been substantially rebuilt in the 1980s and converted into holiday apartments.

Skyreholme Mills, near Appletreewick

Skyreholme Old Mill

This old corn-mill site had gone over to cotton spinning by 1803 when 70 people worked there. In 1822 the mill was to let and could be taken with or without the spinning machinery. It was three storeys high and measured 60 ft by 29 ft with a waterwheel. There were eight carding engines and six mules with

MILL.

TO be LET by PRIVATE CONTRACT, with or without Machinery, and may be entered to at Pleasure, for such a Term of Years as may suit the Taker,—All that MILL or BUILDING, lately used as a Cotton Mill, being 20 Yards long, by 9 and a Half wide, and Three Stories high : together with the Water Wheel, Tumbling Shafts, Goits, Dams, Water and Water Courses thereto belonging, situated and being at Skireholm, in the Township of Appletreewick, in the Parish of Burnsall, and County of York.

☞ The above Mill is about Seven Miles from Skipton, and stands on a powerful and never-failing Stream of Water, and is well calculated for any Business where Power and Room is wanting.

There is in the said Mill at present Six Mules for spinning Cotton of 204 Spindles each, with Eight Carding Engines, and other necessary Utensils for the same, all in good Repair, which the Taker may have with the Mill or not.

For farther Particulars, and to treat for the same, apply to Wm. Holden, or Francis Petty, both residing near the above Premises.

Leeds Mercury, 6 July 1822

204 spindles each. In 1822 Samuel Westerman was listed as a cotton spinner at this mill.

By 1826 the mill had been purchased by Henry & Thomas Bramley & Co. They started building a second mill in 1831, but this was only slowly filled with machines. Large new dams were made for the second mill and water brought over the road to the 39 ft wheel. This second wheel was 5 ft 6 inches wide and the wheel for the old mill was 24 ft by 7 ft. Together both mills employed 81 people in 1833 when they were spinning cotton yarn on mules and throstles. This number went up to 95 for both mills two years later. Bramley & Co. added cotton manufacturing by 1837 and by 1841 calico was being woven at the mill.

The two mills at Skyreholme were to let in 1843, one with a 24 ft wheel and the other with a 39 ft wheel which together generated 24 hp. There was said to be a never-failing spring and a large reservoir though it was admitted that three and a half weeks' work had been lost in the dry summer of 1842. The overlooker would show people round the mills as none of the Bramley family lived near.

Both mills were to let again in 1851 together with a house, garden and 29 cottages. Further details were given about the wheels which had possibly been replaced. The wrought-iron wheels measured 39 ft by 6 ft and 25 ft by 8 ft. In late Victorian times the large wheel was a tourist attraction, with visitors coming from a distance to see it turning on the outside of the mill.

The mills were then taken by Thomas Blakey, still for cotton spinning, but by 1863 they were being used for making paper by Thomas Hagar. Later the mills came into the possession of the Whiteley family who then moved to Pool paper mills.

Today the site is occupied with houses, but walkers going up or down the nearby Trollers Gill can still see the large dam built for the 1831 mill.

Burnsall Mill

The old corn mill at Burnsall was changed over to cotton spinning in 1804 and a new mill was built alongside by William Tempest, the landowner. Richard Chester from Rilston then leased both mills and bought drawing rollers for his new machines from Hattersleys. He may also have had an interest in Scaw Gill Mill in Grassington about 1810. The lease at Burnsall Mill was taken by John Lister from Bingley in 1818 at £30 per year for worsted spinning, but he did not renew it in 1825 when spinning stopped. The corn mill became a sawmill whilst the newer mill was converted into cottages. These cottages face the car park and I have looked at them hundreds of times without realising that they formed an early cotton mill.

Burnsall Mill

Hebden Mill

Hebden Mill was built away from the village on a headland near the river Wharfe. It was built next to a corn mill in 1792 by a partnership consisting of Richard Waddilove of Rilston, Francis Lister of Skipton, Joseph Constantine of Hebden and John Holmes of Burnsall. Waddilove started a second mill at Rilston shortly afterwards, but Waddilove, Lister & Co., cotton manufacturers, insured this mill and contents for £2,500 in 1795. Holmes, a shopkeeper, was possibly the leading partner for in 1793 the firm was listed as J. Holmes & Co., twist spinners, and in 1800 John Holmes & Co. insured the mill and contents for £2,800. The mill was offered for sale in 1800 when the spinning machinery consisted of ten spinning frames and two mules. More machinery could be installed for it was said that, 'The mill will hold eighteen frames on a floor and is situated where plenty of hands may be had'. The partners were prepared to let Hebden Mill if it wasn't sold.

William Parker, one of the three sons of Thomas Parker of Arncliffe Mill took the lease of Hebden Mill but was bankrupt in 1809 and the lease then passed to his brother James, from Low Mill in Gargrave. He insured the mill and its contents for £1,800 in 1810. The mill was then run by Parker and his new partner William Hepworth, until they became bankrupt in 1811, when the mill was put up for sale again. The three-storey mill measured 97 ft by 29 ft within the walls and had a 24 ft by 6 ft waterwheel. The top floor of the mill was taken up with the carding and preparing machinery. The first floor held 16 spinning frames with 48 spindles each, while the ground floor housed workshops. William Hepworth's 1/42 share was offered for sale in 1812.

Richard Waddilove and others advertised the mill to let or be sold in 1821. They were running 16 throstles with 1,440 spindles. As there was no other manufactory in the neighbourhood, hands could be obtained on very moderate terms. About 1830 the mill was taken by Joseph Mason who started some power-loom weaving. Mason was a partner in Coniston Copper Mine, leased coalmines at Hartlington and was also a lead mining agent. By 1837 the mill was taken by Walter Bramley, still for cotton spinning, with a mortgage from J B Sidgwick & Co. of Skipton. He insured the mill and contents for £2,000. In 1840, when the mill came on the market, Bramley was running 2,000 throstle spindles and preparing machines. The extra machinery might have been the reason for the larger waterwheel which measured 25 ft 3 inches by 7 ft. The old 21 ft square corn mill was also for sale. Cottages for mill workers had been built nearby and a 17th-century farmhouse on Brook Street was converted for workers to rent.

By 1851 more than twenty power-loom weavers were living in Hebden, and the census for that year shows they were weaving worsted and cotton cloth. By 1861 the workforce was thirty. A trade directory for 1881 tells us that the mill was being run by Joseph Mason & Brothers who were also running Linton Mill. The mill may have stopped working in the 1890s, but there were two short periods when it was started again. Thomas Moor and Robert Thompson occupied the mill in 1911 and it was running again during World War I with new looms. A Gilkes turbine replaced the waterwheel. According to local information, Hebden Mill was used for power-loom weaving on both occasions and finally stopped in 1927. The upper floor became the Dales Skating Rink in the heyday of roller-skating in the 1930s, but the mill was demolished in 1967. Now, little more than the mill bell with the date 1792 can be seen.

Linton Mill, near Grassington

About the time that John Cunliffe and John Cockshott were planning to use Arkwright-type water frames to spin worsted at Low Mill in Addingham early in 1787, Richard Hargreaves at High Mill, a mile upstream, was also experimenting with mechanised worsted spinning. He had the substantial backing of the Birkbecks from Settle and they invited tenders to build Linton Mill in April 1787 following their partnership agreement in February. This new mill was to be built on the site of an old corn mill. The Birkbecks already had experience of the new spinning processes through their interest in Yore Mill, near Aysgarth Falls. Both the Birkbecks and Hargreaves were Quakers.

This new mill was run by Robert Hargreaves & Co. and, in 1802, as worsted spinners at Linton and Addingham, they warned people not to pay debts to James Hargreaves of Addingham, but at their counting house at Linton or Skipton or to George Scott of Addingham. Samuel Gill, and until 1804, his partner James Parker then leased the mill, or part of it, for cotton spinning. Robert Hargreaves died in 1808, but the mill was still owned by the Birkbecks with W & J Birkbeck described as worsted spinners in 1822. William Simpson was also said to be leasing room and power at Linton Mill at this time.

About 1818 yarn from Linton Mill was being sold to firms in Kidderminster. Worsted spinning continued for many years. In 1835 some 139 people worked at Linton Mill, most of them under 21 and most of them girls apart from some young boys. A new five-storey spinning mill was built, and it may have been following this development that Linton Mill and Grassington Mills were advertised to let or sell in April 1843, when it was suggested that they would be of interest to worsted and cotton spinners. The owners were still J & W Birkbeck & Co. who had been running both this mill and Grassington Low Mill for worsted spinning and power-loom weaving. At that time Linton Mill had a 55 hp waterwheel. Access between the two mills was helped by what was known as the 'tin bridge' across the river Wharfe. This was built in 1814 and gave an easier route to Linton Mill from Grassington. Linton Mill had 22 spinning frames with 1,890 spindles and 121 power looms which were in a new weaving shed.

In Skipton the firm owned a house occupied by the owners, two large warehouses and a shop for 32 combers. As the mills were some distance from the growing centres of the worsted trade Birkbecks stressed the other advantages of the mills. It was said that the poor rates and other rates were low, carriage from Linton to Skipton was cheap at seven and a half pence per pack and hands at reasonable rates were plentiful. In addition the premises were in a thorough state of repair. Overall the properties offered:

… a situation for carrying on to advantage, a large spinning and manufacturing concern either in worsted or cotton, which can rarely be equalled and certainly not surpassed.

The mills were advertised for sale or to let again in November 1843, when it was added that Linton Mill was lit by gas, had its own gas works, comb shop, drying house and 22 cottages for workpeople. The advertisement continued:

The mill has hitherto worked for spinning worsted and weaving by power, and is filled with most excellent machinery for these purposes, in thorough working order and repair; but is well calculated for a cotton mill and will be let either with or without the machinery at present therein.

Linton Mill came on the market again in 1846, when it was leased to Hainsworth, Wright & Patchett from Bradford. The worsted preparing, spinning machinery and power-looms were available to a lessee at valuation and it was hoped that any tenant would take over the mill on or before the 1st December. The 55 hp waterwheel was said to be 'as good as new'.

The mill was then taken by John & Francis Wall of Addingham, who started weaving Orleans cloth with

Leeds Mercury, 23 August 1855

a cotton warp and worsted weft. Wall, Cockshott & Wall gave up the mill in 1855, when it was advertised for lease again. The 55 hp wheel drove spinning machinery as well as all the power looms in the various weaving rooms and there was also a dyehouse.

Linton Mill before the fire of 1912

The 1851 census for Grassington and Linton lists many textile workers with wool combers, worsted power-loom weavers and overlookers prominent among them. In the following years the mill had mixed fortunes and was occupied by a number of firms. Smith, Hartley & Co. moved there from Low Mill at Cowling in the 1850s and then moved on to Skipton. In 1881 Joseph Mason from Skipton rented this mill and also Hebden Mill. John Fielden, also from Skipton, took the mill in 1907, when extra weaving capacity was in demand. In 1909 he leased the water rights upstream to the new Grassington Electric Supply Co., which built a power house and installed a turbine. He also rented part of the mill to Charles Lowcock of Settle who then bought the property and set up both the Linton Mill Estate Company and Linton Mill Manufacturing

Company in 1910. Fire destroyed the old spinning mill in 1912. When it was rebuilt on a smaller scale, but with more weaving capacity added, the waterwheel was replaced with a turbine, which not only drove the line shafting, but also a dynamo for lighting. In the boom following World War I, the weaving sheds were equipped with a 300 hp Newton, Bean & Mitchell steam engine plus a new Gilkes turbine. Francis William Lowcock wove cotton and rayon fabrics for many years until 1959.

When weaving stopped, Francis Lowcock kept much of the machinery intact in the silent mill for about fifteen years, but only used the office. During this time he was visited by Newton Pickles, a mill engineer, who related his experiences to Stanley Graham, who was conducting an oral record of textile mills and their motive power. This interview was in 1979 and has been edited slightly.

Stanley – 'You've another turbine haven't you, up at Grassington?'

Newton – 'Oh aye, up at Lowcock's. He has two. He has a double one, must be about 300 horse power. It's a heck of a thing, Stanley. I couldn't credit that turbine when I first saw it. It's in a great big concrete tank about fifty foot square and it has all the weight of the river on it. I don't want to exaggerate, it's a double one you know, it has a spinner at each end and it's fed from the centre and then you get your vacuum. And they run at a fair speed, do them. Now that single one of course, it's stopped again because he wouldn't pay for having it repaired the first time. Silly old feller!'

Stanley – 'Lowcock's, what are they, are they still a mill?'

Newton – 'They were manufacturers. Grand mill is Linton, make best museum in the country would Linton Mills if the silly old feller 'ud let somebody go in and talk to him and do it. There's everything in that mill. There's a Newton, Bean & Mitchell engine, it'd be the last engine they ever made with drop valves, you know, a drop valve one with a tail end air pump. It ran a great big DC generator about ten feet tall. There's two Paxman diesels, I don't know whether they're six cylinders or eight now. I forgot, one's partially in pieces and t'others all together, with great big DC generators on the ends. There's a 40 horse power turbine that runs a DC generator which used to light his house and heat it. It did that for fifty years, never cost them a penny and when we went to repair it when the bearings conked out he wouldn't pay for it, so I wouldn't go any more. But it's a marvellous set up. Then there's that great big thing down in the concrete cellar, that'd run the blinking lot with a DC generator on it as well as being coupled to all the shafting in the mill. They ran everything off that when there were plenty of water coming down the river, everything, mill, houses, looms, the lot. They even pumped water out of the river for people to drink. It's a shame. In fact I think it's ridiculous. I think someone wants to go along there and plonk an order on it before the scrap chaps get there. There's shafting up and everything.'

No listed building order was placed on the site, so it was cleared for housing in 1983.

Grassington Low Mill

This mill does not draw power from the river Wharfe, but from a small tributary stream on the Grassington side. In earlier times a smelt mill and corn mill were built on opposite sides of this stream. Later the corn mill had many uses, such as soap manufacturing and wood turning but also textiles.

It is not clear when the new mill was built and first used for cotton spinning, but it was for sale in 1804 after it had been run by Samuel Gill.

Gill had a lease until November 1816 and anyone wishing to view the mill had to contact a Mr Wildman of Threshfield or Mr Waddilove of Grassington. Gill's partnership with James Parker of Low Mill, Gargrave, was dissolved at the same time. The mill was for sale in 1813 together with the cotton-spinning machinery. Application had to be made to Mr Wildman.

In 1835 24 people worked at Grassington Low Mill, 18 of them under 21, and the mill was still being used for spinning cotton, but this was soon to change to worsted.

Following earlier advertising in 1839, Linton Mill and Grassington Low Mills were advertised to let or sell again in April 1843, and it was suggested that they would be of interest to worsted and cotton spinners. The owners were still J & W Birkbeck & Co., who had been running both mills for worsted spinning and power-loom weaving. Grassington Mill had a 10 hp wheel with 11 spinning frames holding 1,004 spindles. It is not clear who leased the mill then, but it may have been Smith, Hartley & Co. who were running Linton Mill for a time. Joseph Spencer is recorded as occupying the mill or part of it in 1857.

Between 1878 and 1894 the mill was owned by John Holdsworth & Co. from Shaw Lodge Mills, near Halifax, and in 1881 Edwin Holdsworth was the manager and overlooker living at Low Mill House. This was presumably a small addition to the large mills the firm already ran for producing a wide range of fabrics near Halifax. When Holdsworths gave up the mill in 1894, textile use ceased. However, Clement Holdsworth stayed in the area, bought the Scargill estate near Kettlewell, and became a country gentleman.

Scaw Gill Mill

This small mill, which looks today like a house, was offered for sale in 1813 by its owner John Lupton. By that time it had been converted to a house and cottage, but it had recently been used as a cotton mill. This was probably a jenny mill with only the carding machine powered by a small waterwheel. There would have been a good demand in the area for weft, spun on jennies, as the larger mills all produced warp yarn. The original building, possibly a corn mill, would have been adapted about 1792 and ran until about 1812. In April 1809 the partnership between Moses Wright and William Hardacre, cotton spinners, Grassington, was dissolved. Samuel Gill and then Richard Chester then tried their luck as spinners for a few months, but without success. The building was still being advertised as a former cotton mill in October 1818. Later it was used as a dairy for making butter.

IN GRASSINGTON.
Lot 9. All that Building formerly used as a Cotton-Mill, and called Scaw-Gill-Mill, but at present converted into Cottage-Houses, with the Croft thereto adjoining, now occupied by Mr. John Calvert, or his Undertenants.

Advertisement, Leeds Mercury, 3 October 1818

Kettlewell Mill

Kettlewell, like most Dales villages, had its own corn mill with medieval origins. Unlike many others, however, the corn mill's conversion to cotton spinning came late though it had not been used for several years. In 1805 two cottages alongside the mill were taken by Richard and William Calvert, from Kettlewell, who converted them into a cotton manufactory which indicates handloom weaving. The following year the main mill building was taken and equipped with spinning frames with drawing rollers bought from Hattersleys. Probably a new mill was built on the site alongside the original cottages. At some time the water supply to the mill was enhanced with a new reservoir built at the side of Jacob's Wood. Water was then fed back to the stream where a new weir diverted the supply through a culvert to the mill at a higher level, thus giving more power. This may have been when the new cotton preparing and spinning machines were installed although there was only a 4 hp wheel. Cotton was woven in the village, and in 1816 James Falshaw from Kettlewell attended Manchester to sell his cloth in Cannon Street. Some cottages by the mill were made into a workshop for dandy looms with metal frames. Details of the firms which ran the mill and its size have proved hard to come by. In 1835, only 22 people worked there, most of them children. By 1837 the mill had been taken by John Smith. James Cliffe from Arncliffe Mill may then have occupied it for a few years. The 1841 census recorded several cotton weavers and by 1851 there were six power-loom weavers in Kettlewell. This indicates that power looms were being used at the mill, possibly where the handlooms had been. The noise from these was said to be considerable. Kettlewell Mill closed in 1856 and was offered for sale in the *Leeds Mercury* on the 28th of August 1858.

> **K**ETTLEWELL, near Skipton.—To be SOLD by PRIVATE CONTRACT, the WATER-POWER MILL, in Kettlewell, known as "Kettlewell Mill," and lastly used as a cotton spinning mill, with the iron water wheel, other fixtures, out-buildings, conveniences, and appurtenances belonging to it. To view the property app'y to Mr. Wm. Marshall, Farmer, Kettlewell; or to Mr. John Harker, Schoolmaster, Grassington; and to treat for the purchase, to Mr. T. H. Battye, Solicitor, Market-place, Huddersfield. C 11169

It had lately been used for spinning cotton, had an iron waterwheel and the sale included some outbuildings. Application had to be made to William Marshall, a farmer in Kettlewell or John Harker, a schoolmaster in Grassington. The mill was probably not used again and was demolished in 1876, the stone being used to build a shop on the other side of the road.

Arncliffe Mill

The old corn mill at Arncliffe on Cowside Beck was advertised for sale in October 1785 when it was said to be 'a very convenient situation for establishing a cotton manufactory'. It wouldn't be seen as convenient now, but in 1791 Thomas Parker started building a four-storey cotton-spinning mill there and bought additional land two years later. He had been a publican in Keighley, married the daughter of Betty Hudson, the owner of Damside Mill in Keighley, and set out as a cotton spinner and manufacturer. Parker insured his mill and machinery for £2,000 in November 1792 and added a house, warehouse, cottages and a stable which can still be seen by the road. Spindles and flyers, possibly for new spinning frames, were bought in 1798. Purchases from Hattersleys continued for several years. Parker took his son and namesake as a partner but their partnership as cotton spinners at Arncliffe was dissolved in July 1801 with any debts to be paid by the father. Parker junior returned to Keighley to manage his grandmother's mill.

Thomas Parker senior continued as a cotton spinner and manufacturer, having some of his yarn woven locally, but was bankrupt in 1815. His mill was four storeys high and measured 60 ft by 28 ft and could be used for spinning cotton, worsted or flax. Included in the sale were ten cottages, a house and stable, land, shares in two lead mines and a barn at Starbotton in Wharfedale.

According to the practice at the time, all his possessions were also for sale. In the mill were spinning frames and throstles, warping mills, bobbins, a lathe and tools, iron and brass and upwards of 200 calico warps, reeds and healds. He had six valuable draught horses, a new wagon, two carts, a cow and pigs and hay to feed them with. In his house were four-post bedsteads, mahogany tables, a pianoforte, carpets, glasses and china as well as a variety of kitchen furniture and brewing vessels.

James Cliffe, who may have been a calico manufacturer in Embsay, then took Arncliffe Mill and insured the mill, machinery and stock for £1,000 in 1820, when he was described as a cotton twist and weft spinner. In 1822 he was described also as a cotton manufacturer, perhaps having yarn woven locally, but he was just a spinner in 1833. The working day started at six in the morning until seven at night with one hour for lunch. Kettlewell Fair and Christmas Day were the only two holidays. Some 31 people worked at the mill in 1835.

James Cliffe's cotton machinery and household effects were to be auctioned on the 26th and 27th of September, 1842. The machinery could be seen running prior to the sale and included all the machines to take raw cotton and make it into yarn. The spinning machines consisted of 12 throstles with 112 spindles each and a pair of mules. Included was a horse and cart which no doubt occupied the stable which can be seen today. Again there occurred the sad story of the bankrupt's possessions being listed, his chairs, sofas, tea trays and brewing utensils.

No buyer came forward so the mill was put up for auction again on the 17th November at the Tennant's Arms at Kilnsey. This time the dimensions of the rooms were given. It had five storeys with the basement being 26 ft by 28 ft, the first floor 35 ft by 28 ft and the other three floors 48 ft by 28 ft. The wheel measured 22 ft by 6 ft and had a 21 ft fall from a never-failing stream.

The mill was then taken by Richard Brennand and towards the end of its life all the yarn went to Colne. It was still running in 1869, but ceased production in the 1870s. The mill was advertised for sale in July 1875 together with 12 cottages and a five-horse stable. It had a new waterwheel and was said to be suitable for doublers, spinners and manufacturers. Application had to be made to Briggs Brothers of Daubhill Mill in Bolton. It is likely that the mill was not sold, but gradually decayed to be a considerable eyesore.

In the 1920s the mill was bought and turned into an attractive private house by the removal of the top two floors. The small millpond at the back of the house was turned into a sunken garden, but the outline of the large dam further up the valley can still be seen from the road to Malham.

Washburn Valley

West End

West End Village

Capelshaw Beck and the Washburn provided the sites for five mills from around 1800. During the seventeenth and eighteenth centuries this area, like many others, produced woollen and linen textiles. Weavers worked in their own homes and also in small loom-shops set up by the wealthier manufacturers. Linen was spun and woven in the area which was part of the flax-processing industry centred on Knaresborough, where there were said to be 200 looms in 1808, producing 400 pieces each week. Though the earliest mills were built for spinning cotton, they soon changed to flax. This was brought about by the distance from the cotton market in Manchester and the needs of the local handloom weavers. A combination of local linen merchants with capital, strong demand from local weavers, availability of labour, suitable sites and low freight costs for flax from the Baltic via Hull prompted expansion. The speed of this development around 1800 indicates that the linen trade was very profitable. New mills were built on corn-mill sites and the construction of mill workers' cottages created new villages. Widows with large numbers of children were the ideal tenants for the new cottages. Westhouse Mill, one of the largest mills built in the Dales, imported child labour from London. Two apprentice houses were built for them.

The spinning of flax continued until the slump of the late 1830s when competition from cheaper cotton cloth cut into the market for linen. Another trade depression in the late 1840s caused many mills to cease trading. In nearby Nidderdale large flax and hemp mills were built later in the century, but they were near the new railway and concentrated on the production of thread, rope and twine, for which there was a huge demand. Ropewalks were constructed and lasted until well after the Second World War. Low Mill at West End, the oldest Washburn mill, was re-equipped to spin hemp for ropes about 1880 which brought the end of textile production in the valley.

From the end of the nineteenth century, West End was often known as the 'deserted village' before it was flooded to create Thruscross reservoir, as the houses, church, post office and mills were all abandoned and derelict. Industry had moved away, but in the early part of the century there was a range of textile occupations, such as handloom weaving, as well as mill work. For instance in 1822 two linen manufacturers were listed in Fewston, Thomas Buck and William Demain, and they would have employed many people in the area. However, as time went on, the fortunes of the various firms which owned or leased the four mills in West End had a considerable impact on the hamlet as there was really no alternative work. If a mill stopped when trade was bad, the workers had to move away, particularly when power looms were introduced elsewhere. The temporary closure of Low Mill in 1850 cut the population by one-third and in 1851 some 32 out of 41 houses in and around West End were empty. The temporary closure of Westhouse Mill, just down the valley and at the same, time resulted in 45 out of 61 houses being unoccupied.

The sequence of ownership and tenants at the three lower mills in West End is hard to establish. Sale notices for a lease often said simply that the mill was at West End without saying which one. Also there was multiple occupancy, particularly at Low Mill, which was easily divided into separate sections. In addition, John Patrick, the manager at Low Mill, married the leading partner's daughter. He acquired his own partners and then went on to buy or lease the two nearby mills. The first of these was built by Walkers from Low Mill so was then called High Mill, but many 20th-century observers called it Patrick's Mill and the next mill, Patrick's Little Mill. Akeds referred to their mill for some years as High Mill as it was the furthest up the valley, but after a partial rebuild renamed it Croft House Factory. Some 20th-century observers, not knowing this, have used the owners' names instead of the given name which has led to confusion. It is doubtful that the Aked family would have called their own mill Aked's Mill.

Westhouse Mill, Blubberhouses

Blubberhouses Church and Westhouse Mill

In 1791 a site suitable for a cotton mill was advertised in one of the Leeds newspapers. This was Blubberhouses Corn Mill, which was near the 'grand road' from Skipton to Knaresborough and where it was said the best stone for building was near to hand. However, the new mill, started in 1797, was to be used for spinning flax, and was built alongside the corn mill. In the following year Colbeck, Watson & Co. advertised for flax dressers in a Leeds paper and in the same year bought iron components from Hattersleys of Keighley. In 1798 the owners insured the mill with the Sun Company. It was one of the largest built in the Dales with five storeys plus attics and eventually a whole range of ancillary buildings. Though surrounded by carefully prepared parkland, it dominated the landscape, as can be seen from the old photograph taken from the road near Blubberhouses church.

There were three good reasons why the mill was built here, but unfortunately progress eventually made them redundant: firstly the water supply from the Washburn, secondly the site on the main road from Knaresborough and easy access to flax supplies which came through Hull and thirdly the huge demand for yarn from the local linen weavers. In later years the advance of steam power with the need to be near cheap coal supplies, the distance from canals and later rail transport together with changes in markets and the growth of factory production in cities made the site uneconomic.

The original partnership of five consisted of Thomas Colbeck from Keighley, who was a partner in Goit Stock Cotton Mill near Bingley in 1797, and Rowland Watson, who was a lawyer in Keighley, but who had entered into partnerships in two Keighley cotton-spinning mills, Greengate Mill in 1784 and Stubbing House Mill in 1789. Other partners were William and John Holdsworth with Jacob Wilks, a Knaresborough linen manufacturer, and William Ellis, a leading Yorkshire cotton spinner, who joined later. The early mortgage obtained to fund the building of the mill was from John Greenwood of Keighley, a partner with William Ellis in many textile enterprises. This passed to Chippendale, Netherwood & Carr, the Skipton bankers, in 1808.

The mill appeared to be successful in the early years and insurance valuations rose as more buildings were added when Wilks and Ellis joined the partnership in 1805. A large warehouse was built, with the stock and utensils it held insured for £6,000 in 1807. The original mill was doubled in size in 1812 with a consequent need for a new waterwheel and water supply. By 1816 a steam engine had been installed together with a weaving shop equipped with handlooms, a counting house, thread shop, bleaching house and drying house for warps. This expansion, at a time when flax supplies from the Baltic were often interrupted because of the French wars, possibly anticipated an increase in trade when hostilities finished. This was not to be and Colbeck, Ellis & Co. were bankrupt in 1816. In June the following year all the household goods and furniture of Thomas Colbeck were for sale. He clearly lived in some style for the sale lasted four days. The young apprentices who were now out of work were taken in by the township of Fewston, much to the displeasure of the local ratepayers. Some of William Ellis's considerable assets had to be sold to pay his creditors and his debts impacted on his partners, the Greenwoods, at other mills.

Although the rural population was much larger than it is today, more child labour was required at the mill than was available locally. Cottages were built near the mill to attract families and eventually totalled 37. In addition there were two apprentice houses for pauper children brought from London, one for boys and one for girls. The parents of Robert Collyer, who has been quoted earlier, lived there before taking a small cottage when they married. The High Apprentice House is now a private house.

The bankruptcy of Colbeck, Ellis & Co. left extensive debts to banks in Skipton and Wakefield as well as trade debts of £8,000. When Chippendale, Netherwood & Carr took over the mill in 1820, they had to take on some of the debt, but as they were partners in the Skipton bank, they presumably felt that keeping the mill operating was the only choice. The bankruptcy proceedings continued for many years with land and farms belonging to the original partners still being sold in 1822.

TO BLEACHERS, &c.

TO BE LET, for a Term of Years, and and entered upon Immediately,—All that BUILDING, adjoining the West-House Factory, in the Parish of Fewstone; before appropriated to various Chymical Purposes; with every Convenience and Accommodation for carrying on the Business of a Bleacher, in the most commodious and extensive Manner; together with a good HOUSE, and any Quantity of LAND that may be required for such an Undertaking.

Any Person desirous of embarking in such a Concern, will find that a constant Supply of Work may be obtained from the adjoining Factory.

Mr. Michael Robinson, of the West-House Factory, will shew the Premises; and further Particulars may be had on Application to Messrs Chippendale and Co. of Skipton.—West-House, Sept. 5th. 1820.

Leeds Mercury 9 September 1820

When production started again in 1820, an attempt to rent out the bleaching section of the mill was made and it was added that a constant supply of work would come from the adjoining factory. This building was:

before appropriated to various chymical purposes; with every convenience and accommodation for carrying on the business of a bleacher.

In 1836, £3,000 was paid off the £8,000 mortgage and in the same year Robinson Chippendale died. His trustees sold his share to the sons of the other partners, Christopher Netherwood and John Carr. In 1839 Netherwood bought out Carr's share, added gas lighting and he went to live in the house by the mill, but trading conditions worsened in 1841 when France taxed yarn imports. He became increasingly dependent on the Craven Bank, owing them £35,000 by 1843, plus a mortgage of £5,000 and decided to sell the mill. The mill and 547-acre estate were first advertised in February 1843, but neither was taken despite many fulsome advertisements. The mill could hold 14,000 flax spindles and was turning out 1,400 to 1,500 bundles of yarn per week ranging from 10 leas to 120 leas. The power-looms had all been purchased in the last four years. The 30 hp steam engine was used only when there was a shortage of water as the mill held an iron wheel measuring 39 ft by 10 ft and a wooden wheel 33 ft by 11 ft. There were 37 cottages, a farm house, bleach works, stabling for 14 horses, two carriage houses and the house occupied by Christopher Netherwood which had been recently enlarged and repaired. The five-storey corn mill and drying kiln were included. It is possible that flax had been bought from Messrs Beadle, Sykes & Co., flax merchants of Hull.

In May 1846 the whole estate was offered for sale again, this time in five lots. The first lot was the water- and steam-powered mill together with the bleach works, corn mill, 14 cottages, a large house, a barn, land and weaving shops. The total amount of land was now down to 152 acres so Christopher Netherwood had been able to realise some of his assets. Lot 2 was a farm and High Prentice House with its outbuildings. Lot 3 was some land. Lot 4 consisted of cottages and Lot 5 was the Low

Prentice House, now occupied as seven cottages plus some other cottages. A few weeks later the sale was postponed, but it was announced again in August. A further delay meant that Westhouse Mill was finally put up for auction in Leeds on the 6th April, 1847. To ease the burden of the cost, any purchaser could have a mortgage of £10,000 to £12,000. Netherwood's problems took another turn when some men purporting to visit the mill to look at the machinery stole some brass and iron castings. Eventually the machinery was sold by the bank together with some land.

No takers were found for the mill until 1850, when it was sold to John Threlfall, a cotton spinner, who was also running Low Mill at West End. However, his father, William Threlfall from Low Mill at Addingham became bankrupt so the venture collapsed. The mill and all the other lots were for sale again in September 1851, when John Threlfall was on hand to show prospective purchasers round the property. The mill had already been equipped with cotton-spinning machines, but it was said that the mill could be used for worsted spinning.

Another change in direction came in 1856 when Crowthers of Halifax bought Westhouse Mill, the old corn mill and fourteen cottages and re-equipped it again, this time to spin silk. This was a fairly small-scale venture and a half share was sold to John Wilson from Earlsheaton near Dewsbury for £3,500 in 1863. There had been an expansion of silk spinning in West Yorkshire, but at this remote valley it did not succeed and the mill was closed by 1870. It was then bought by Leeds Corporation and demolished, with the stone used in the construction of new reservoirs. Today only some of the watercourses can be seen.

Low Mill, West End

John Walker from Silver Mill in Otley, an early cotton mill, joined with his father-in-law Joseph Hardcastle, William Maude, Robert Thomson and Richard Holdsworth to buy the corn mill at West End in 1791 and on the site built this large mill. By 1796 it was valued at £4,550 and their profits encouraged them to build High Mill (later Patrick's Mill) a short distance upstream in 1800. The mill, wheel and machinery were insured for £1,700 in 1801. When Walker & Co. registered their mill in 1803 they reported that they employed about 90 persons with only two apprentices. At the time they were running 1,540 spindles, part-driven by the waterwheel, and others, probably jennies, by hand. There was no night shift at the mill. By 1805 Holdsworth, Thomson and Maude had left the partnership and in 1807 the mills were to let by auction and had already been changed to spin flax. Walker & Co. then gave up running the mill themselves and leased it to a flax spinner, possibly Christopher Smith.

Michael Meek then took the mill. He was a linen manufacturer and spirit merchant with large premises on the High Street in Knaresborough and also owned land and property in Sedgefield, County Durham. He was bankrupt in 1824 and his flax and tow preparing and spinning machinery at Low Mill was for sale the following year by his assignees together with the lease. He had 14 flax spinning frames with 708 spindles and 13 tow frames. The four-storey mill was said to measure 94 ft by 57 ft and the sale included 19 cottages. Three years of the lease were left and the rent was £284 p.a.

Meek must have been allowed to continue running Low Mill by his assignees until the lease ran out, for it was advertised to let again in 1827, this time by the owner, Charles Walker from Otley, John Walker's son. The new lease was to run from the 1st February 1828. The measurements of the mill differed and it was quoted as being 102 ft by 34 ft, which is more likely. The mill had a 24 ft wheel and was capable of spinning 250 bundles of flax a week. Some land and stables were rented by Messrs Patrick & Smith.

A number of flax and tow spinning frames together with the preparing machinery and also the whitesmith's tools, lathes, anvils and bellows to maintain them were for sale at West End Mills in January, 1828. Application had to be made to John Patrick & Co. at West End or Robinson & Dearlove in Knaresborough, who were probably Michael Meek's assignees. They then ran two-thirds of the mill for a few years

In 1833 Low Mill was run by Vipont & Co., who had moved from Castle Mill in Knaresborough, and by the early 1840s by Vipont & Whiteley, who employed about 70 workers, including twenty in the flax-dressing shop. It was then taken by Whiteley & Brown for spinning flax, but they were bankrupt by 1846 and the mill was idle with the cottages near the mill empty. When their machinery was finally to be auctioned on 16th December, the top floor of the mill gave way. Though there were injuries, no one was killed. A second auction was arranged for April and included 13 double spinning frames, preparing machinery and engineer's tools. In 1847 William Threlfall, who was running Low Mill at Addingham, leased the mill for £200 a year and turned the mill back to spin cotton. Threlfall's sons, John and William, took over the lease in 1848, but their father's bankruptcy in 1850 caused the closure of the mill. They had hoped to lease Westhouse Mill as well, but both projects failed. Part of the mill might have been occupied by Thomas Lister, who moved machinery here from Patrick's Mill. However, he may not have started cotton spinning as he moved his machinery again, this time to Good Intent Mill at Embsay by April 1850.

Low Mill at West End

Robert Benson and Richard Pullan, who had leased New York Mill near Summerbridge in Nidderdale in 1854, decided to lease West End Low Mill in 1857 and revive flax spinning in the valley. By 1861 they were employing 33 workers at the mill, so it was not a large enterprise. The mill was then taken by Francis Thorpe & Co. until 1868, when it was leased by Thomas Gill. He had trained as a mill mechanic, later became a partner in a textile machinery-making foundry and patented one of his inventions. About 1880 he changed Low Mill over to spin heavy yarns from hemp and tow and nearly 100 years of textile production stopped in West End. Thomas Gill's five sons took over the firm and rebuilt New York Mill, near Summerbridge as their main production unit. This new mill had water turbines and electricity when it was opened in 1890. The machinery from Low Mill was then transferred to New York Mill. The third generation of the Walker family tried to sell Low Mill in November 1890, but failed and the building was acquired by Leeds Corporation.

Patrick's Mill or High Mill, West End

At times it is very difficult to be accurate about which firms ran Low Mill and which Patrick's Mill, or as Walkers called it, High Mill. At times West End Mills were mentioned as though they were run in tandem. Originally this mill was built by Walker and Co. from Low Mill in 1800 as they expanded their cotton business. In 1803 Walker & Co. had no apprentices amongst their 30 employees at this mill, but they were running 516 spindles. The manager at Low Mill, John Patrick, married John Walker's daughter and became a tenant at this mill in 1812. In 1822 he bought the mill and the next mill up the valley. The partnership between John Patrick of Otley, Stephen Smith of West End, William Robinson of Knaresborough and Robert Dearlove of Knaresborough, who traded as John Patrick & Co., was dissolved on the 21st October 1829. Robinson and Dearlove had been partners with John Marshall in Leeds, one of the country's leading flax spinners. Robinson continued flax spinning at the mill until 1836, when he was bankrupt, though John Patrick still owned the mill. His machinery included 15 frames with 548 spindles as well as all the preparing and workshop machinery. A fortnight later the mill was offered to let. The mill was then said to have a 45 ft by 5 ft wheel. The mill and machinery was taken by Joseph Moore, who possibly bought some new tow frames from Dockroy & Pinder, machine makers, of Leeds. Moore failed a year later and the machinery at the mill was for sale again. This sale included not only Moore's preparing and spinning machinery with 480 spindles, but the shafting, pulleys and straps to connect the waterwheel to the machinery. Patrick's Mill was then leased by Henry Hogg from John Patrick, but offered to let in 1841. The four-storey mill measured 90 ft by 29 ft inside and was powered by a 45 ft wheel with an 'abundant supply of water'. Though the mill had been used for flax spinning and still held the flax machinery, it was said to be 'well calculated for worsted or cotton'.

Thomas Lister, who had been a chandler in Addingham, took this mill in 1847 and started to install cotton-spinning machinery. When Low Mill became available a year or so later, he moved his machinery there and textile production may not have continued afterwards.

I remember helping with a survey of the watercourse for Patrick's Mill before it was submerged under Thruscross Reservoir. The site was densely wooded, but we could trace the goit which must have finished in a launder to the mill and the large waterwheel.

Little Mill, West End

This mill was run by Daniel Garforth & Co. for cotton spinning from 1805 or before. In that year Garforth bought flyers and spindles for his spinning frames from Hattersleys of Keighley. In March 1807, a sale at his property included horses and cows, as well as ten bales of cotton and a pack of cotton twist. In 1811 Samuel Crompton's census of spinning machines showed that 'D Garfoot' of West End had 20 throstles with 72 spindles each, giving a total of 1,440. It is not known who ran the mill after this, but John Patrick bought the mill in 1822 and ran it in tandem with his other mill just down the valley. In January 1841, Patrick's Mill and Little Mill were to let. The two-storey mill measured 63 ft by 17½ ft inside and had two 20 ft waterwheels, one on each floor. It had lately been used for spinning flax and contained between 500-600 spindles for coarse flax and tow. Also to let were some cottages and land. The mill would be let with or without the machinery. It is doubtful if the mill was leased as trade was bad and it later became a sawmill.

Patrick's Little Mill, West End

High Mill or Croft House Factory or Aked's Mill, West End

This was a substantial mill which appeared to be in the hands of the Aked family for nearly all its years and so was given their name by later observers. Reputedly built in 1809 by John and James Aked from Halifax, the mill was for sale in 1816 when it had been used for spinning flax. Besides the preparation machinery there were 312 spindles. The mill was said to be well supplied with water and had an excellent dam. William Aked, of Lawnd House in Otley owned the mill, but application had to be made to John Aked on the premises. The mill was not sold, but was to let the following year when the number of spindles had increased to 420.

Leeds Mercury, 25 May 1816

In 1824 another advertisement gave some details of two buildings. There was a 75 ft fall to the three waterwheels and the mills were said to be 'capable of spinning upon an average, upwards of 300 bundles of line and tow yarn per week'. The machinery, which was nearly new, included 13 spinning frames with 736 spindles as well as the usual preparation machines. The mills were said to be 'in full work, excellent repair and well supplied with hands'. As well as the mills, there were 15 cottages, a dry house, warehouse and farm. James Aked, the owner, would show prospective purchasers round the mill and would also lease the machinery, but application had to be made to William Aked of West Parade, Halifax.

James and William Aked advertised the mill to let again in 1836. They were running 1,000 flax spindles and believed that there was sufficient power for another 500. They said that the mill 'offers a very advantageous opportunity to everyone wishing to commence the spinning of fine flax yarns, as the tenant may either purchase the machinery at a very modest valuation or rent it, along with the mill and farm'. There are reports that there was a serious fire at the mill in 1838, but it was rebuilt.

In 1841 the mill and machinery were to let and the mill was named as Croft House Factory. William Aked had moved to Scotland Mill at Adle, near Leeds and the new mortgagee was William Emmett, a paper maker from Halifax. The current tenant was Thomas Bielby and the mill and machinery were said to be in excellent repair and condition. A steam engine had been added to power the mill and a new tenant could also take a house, five cottages, a warehouse, stable and 14 acres of land. The low-pressure steam engine was for sale in 1844 when William Aked was selling some machinery at Scotland Mill. The following year the whole mill was for sale or lease. With three waterwheels fed by two spacious reservoirs, the mill held about 1,000 flax-spinning spindles using the hot water principle and was still occupied by Thomas Bielby. Three months later another advertisement warned that if the mill was not let or sold the machinery would be sold separately. That probably happened and the mill was not used again for textile production.

Around Settle

Settle Area

Converted corn mills began the mechanised cotton trade in and around Settle during the late eighteenth century. Some buildings were used only for cotton; others later changed to flax or worsted. Though cotton weaving was widespread, the records relating to it are sparse since the handloom weavers were often self-employed and had other occupations. However, in 1806 the partnership between Jeremiah Smith and Richard Heelis as cotton manufacturers was dissolved with Henry Armitstead the witness. Smith had been a partner in the cotton spinning partnership formed to run Stainforth Mill in 1792. Settle had twenty cotton weavers in 1803 and Long Preston twenty-four, while in 1809 a Halifax newspaper noted that good quantities of calicoes were made in the district. Another writer commented that 'towards the end of the last century (1800) and the beginning of this, almost every village in Craven had its cotton mill where now hardly a stone is left to tell the story of a vanished industry'. Before the introduction of cotton spinning, hand-knitting had been an important industry, but the new turnpike road between Keighley and Kendal and the new employment opportunities confined it to the more remote dales.

Settle was the most important cotton town in the area with five mills in 1835, which employed 333 people. Langcliffe Mill was the first to be built and worked the longest. This concentration of mills was commented on by contemporary writers. In 1815, 'The cotton mills here, and in the vicinity, employ a great many hands, especially in the winter'. In 1822, 'There are several cotton mills in which the labouring classes find themselves compensated for the deficiency of work in the fields'.

Weaving the locally-spun cotton yarn on handlooms would seem to have continued well after power looms were introduced elsewhere in the 1820s. One example from Austwick is given in the North Craven Heritage Trust's Journal for 1995. If the handloom weavers were put out of work, they became a burden on the local parish. It was therefore in everyone's interest to keep them employed, so a group of local men set up a sort of co-operative 'to enquire into and purchase warps and weft and also to employ what number of looms they think proper in each house'. Starting in 1826, some 6,135 cotton pieces were woven in Austwick in the first year and this success led to the building of a weaving shed. The small subsidy for each piece had kept people in employment and a further weaving shed was built about 1850. By the 1870s handloom weaving was almost finished, but this example, which was probably typical, shows how handloom weaving continued in Craven well after power-loom weaving became common.

Settle missed out on the development of canals, but when the North-Western Railway was proposed in 1845, the provisional committee included many local people with textile interests. These were William Clayton, Langcliffe; Thomas Redmayne, Settle; Hornby Roughsedge, Bentham; John Dewhurst, Skipton; George Sergeantson, Hanlith and Thomas Birkbeck, Settle.

Fleet's Mill, Long Preston

This three-storey mill, which survives as a barn, was built about 1792 by Robert Serjeantson and a partner named Procter. They insured their 'weft cotton manufactory' for £150 and the contents for £250. The next year Serjeantson was joined by his brother-in-law William Tatham, and when

Window detail

they added new machinery they increased the cover to £1,000. The mill was for sale in 1812 and had a windmill for returning water to the dam.

Both Fleet's Mill and Lower Mill came on the market in 1828. The only detail about Fleet's Mill was that there was also an acre of land with it, which would have held the dam. Cotton spinning may have finished at this time.

Lower Mill, Long Preston

This mill was built shortly after Fleet's Mill and was run in conjunction with it. The buildings were only a few hundred yards apart. Lower Mill was built by Robert Serjeantson and his brother–in-law William Tatham who insured the mill and contents for £1,000 in 1792. In 1812 it had a steam engine as well as a waterwheel. In January 1814, both mills, and the machinery in them, were for sale. The four-storey Lower Mill also had outbuildings and a house nearby while Fleets Mill had an acre of land. Lower Mill had the advantage of the 5 hp steam engine and the machinery included mules and throstles. It was said that 'These mills are situate in a neighbourhood where hands may easily be had at reasonable wages and present an eligible offer to a manufacturer whose consumption of calico materials is about ten cwt weekly which these mills are capable of turning off'. Application had to be made to John Wood in Manchester or Mr Heelis in Long Preston.

In 1828 both this mill and Fleet's Mill were for sale. Lower Mill was described as a substantial cotton mill, four storeys high with outbuildings and a dam. No references have been found after this date and the mill was destroyed by a flood in 1881.

Rathmell Mill

This mill was an early Arkwright-type mill measuring 36 ft by 27 ft with a 17 ft wheel. It was built before 1797 and occupied until then by the firm of Brown & Clark though previous occupants may have been Armitstead, Brown & Co. It would have been built for water frames, but by 1797 it had six jennies. By 1811 it was used for grinding corn and later it became a joiner's shop.

Runley Bridge Mill, Settle

James Brennan, a Settle merchant, built this three-storey mill in 1786 on the site of an earlier corn mill. Later that year he insured the mill for £400 and the utensils and stock for £600. By 1791 it had passed to the brothers John, James and Thomas Thornber of Colne. Thomas took over Dog Kennel Mill a few years later and then with his brother James, William Garth and Giles Redmayne also ran Bridge End Mill. The firm running Runley Bridge Mill traded as John Thornber & Co., and were cotton manufacturers as well as spinners, using both jennies and frames. In 1810 the mill was advertised for sale on the death of James Thornber. One three-storey building measured 18 yards by 9½ yards and was powered by a 21 ft by 4 ft wheel. Another three-storey building which was used for spinning weft measured 11 yards by 7½ yards while a third, also three storeys, was 10 yards square with a 15 by 4 ft wheel. Four cottages plus workshops were included in the sale. The machinery included eight water frames and eight jennies.

The mill was then leased by James Procter & Sons, who rebuilt part of it after a fire caused by one of the machines in August 1825. In 1840 John Thornber & Co. were listed at this mill, but spinning stopped about 1847. In 1856 the mill, dam and cottages were unoccupied, but owned by John Birkbeck. Later the buildings were converted for agricultural use. Now they have been converted into a house.

King's Mill or Snuff Mill, Settle

Originally this was a tobacco and snuff mill, which was advertised for sale in 1820 by William Holgate. In 1825 it was taken by Thomas Procter & Sons from Runley Bridge Mill, who ran both mills. A fire in 1830 necessitated complete rebuilding and this new mill had a 20 hp wheel and employed 125 people in 1833. Steam power was added at some time and Procters continued until the 1850s when it was taken by Stephen Parkinson. By 1881 John Kelly and Henry Hartley were spinning cotton waste here and also at Scalegill Mill, near Kirkby Malham. At some point a few power-looms were installed, but textile production stopped before World War I. Now the building has been converted into flats.

Scaleber Mill or Dog Kennel Mill, Settle

In 1790 this mill was insured for £200 with the contents at £297 by John Thornber from Runley Bridge Mill. It appeared to be used for cotton spinning in conjunction with Runley Bridge Mill by the Thornber family, but was taken by Faulkner & Co. in the 1830s. Thomas Brennand took the mill by 1837 for cotton spinning and may have bought it in 1844 with the help of a mortgage from William Clayton from Langcliffe Mill together with George and Mary Hartley and John Hartley from King's Mill. By 1854 it had become a mechanic's shop.

Bridge End Mill, Settle

Before cotton spinning started in 1785, William Buck had a forge on the site and, among other things, made the ironwork for the waterwheel at Langcliffe Mill two miles upstream. Forge work continued and Buck made textile machinery both for his own use and for sale. Early in 1785, his brother, Thomas Buck, also a whitesmith, and Thomas Wilkinson, David Jay and Thomas Ritchie, all from Leeds, joined him as partners to start cotton spinning. This ended in November 1785 when a Leeds newspaper carried the announcement that the partnership of Wilkinson, Bucks, Jay & Co., who had been spinning cotton at Settle Bridge Mill for some time, had been dissolved. The Buck brothers appeared to be better at making spinning machines than operating them for a profit and in 1793 were listed as being worsted spinners and machine makers. In 1796 they made the first worsted-spinning machines for Pease & Co. of Darlington and in 1800 were making combing machines as well as worsted-spinning frames. In that year six worsted frames with 300 spindles plus a combing machine and cotton machinery were for sale at Bridge End Mill. The mill was described as a cotton twist mill and was for sale or lease. The mill was then bought by Edmund Armitstead who was a cotton merchant. He was bankrupt in 1808.

Bridge End Mill, Settle

At some point Claytons & Walshman from Langcliffe Mill took the mill and spun cotton here until at least 1849 when they became bankrupt and the property was for sale again. This time it was described as a cotton mill, factory and warehouse. The machinery in the mill consisted of two scutchers, 14 carding engines, three heads of drawing, one doubler, 6½ pairs of hand mules with 4,160 spindles and two stretching frames with 256 spindles. Bridge End Mill was owned by Richard Bashall and tenanted by Scott & Holden from August 1852. They were cotton manufacturers, but textile production stopped a few years later and the building became a sawmill.

Langcliffe Mill

Langcliffe Mill near Settle

The success of their first mill in Keighley persuaded Claytons & Walshman to build another at Langcliffe, near Settle, this time without a licence from Richard Arkwright. Robert Walshman's father, Thomas, had been a partner with Arkwright and others at the mill at Birkacre near Chorley, which rioters destroyed in 1779. There was no opposition to the new mills in Yorkshire so he recruited John, George and William Clayton, calico printers from Bamber Bridge in Lancashire, to join him in these new ventures. Robert's sister Ann was married to William Clayton. They bought an old corn mill on the Ribble and started to build at the end of 1783. More land was bought in 1784, 'for the purpose of making a cut through and carrying the water from the River Ribble to the intended cotton works'. Part of the building cost was met by profit from Keighley, Low Mill.

Spinning on frames made by local craftsmen started before the mill was complete and children were brought from Keighley to help train the local youngsters. The mill was finished in November 1784, when £7. 7s. was paid for a dinner and £2 2s 6d. for ale enjoyed by the workmen and children.

As with many rural cotton mills, labour was a serious problem, and Claytons & Walshman sought to get round this by building cottages and advertising for families to take them.

Notice is hereby given

That Messrs Clayton & Walshman, cotton manufacturers, in order to accommodate work people are now erecting a number of convenient cottages at Langcliffe Place, which will be ready to enter at Mayday next.

Any people with large families that are desirous to have them employed, and can come well recommended, may be assured of meeting with every reasonable encouragement by applying to Messrs Clayton & Walshman, at Langcliffe aforesaid, or at their cotton works at Keighley. April 10th 1787

These cottages were included in the insurance of all the premises in 1788 when the mill and machinery were each covered for £1,500, a warehouse and cottages for £200, the contents for £500 and a range of tenements adjoining the mill for £250.

After Robert Walshman's death in 1793 the mill was run by the Clayton family. In 1818 a new, much larger mill was added and the machinery alone was insured for £5,200, some parts for cards being bought from Kirkstall Forge. William Clayton & Son employed 203 people at the mill in 1833. By then the firm had installed a 30 hp steam engine, which was used in dry weather, but the 40 hp waterwheel provided most of the power. The mill was used for cotton spinning and weaving.

Claytons & Wilson failed in 1849, so the house, Langcliffe Place, together with Langcliffe Mills and Bridge End Mill, came on the market. Besides the waterwheel there was a 40 hp steam engine. The spinning machinery consisted of seven pairs of self-acting mules with 5,494 spindles and 18½ pairs of hand mules with

Leeds Mercury, 18 Sept. 1852

14,032 spindles. The mill was bought by Richard Bashall from Walton-le-Dale in Lancashire and on the 31st August 1852 he leased the two mills plus Threaps Shed to Henry Scott, James Holden and Christopher Holden who were cotton manufacturers. In 1854 two firms, Richard Brown & Co. and Scott & Holden, were spinning cotton at Langcliffe. Brown was also running the cotton mill in Burton-in-Lonsdale at this time. In 1855 it was reported that Richard Bashall had failed, and with the mill stopped, large numbers of villagers had moved to Accrington for work. By 1857 John Hartley had taken the mill for a few years. In 1861 the mills were bought by Lorenzo Christie who brought in labour from Devon, Cornwall, Norfolk and Manchester. He was followed by Hector Christie, cotton spinner and doubler, who had premises in Salford. Christies contributed generously to the educational and sports facilities in the area. By the end of the century the waterwheels were replaced with turbines made by John Turnbull of Glasgow, one of 90 hp and the other 180 hp. These were again replaced with a Gilkes of Kendal turbine. A steam engine was added to provide power when water supplies were low and this was also connected to the line shafting. In 1892 this was a horizontal twin, single crank engine made by Wood & Co.

Hector Christie

In 1898 the Fine Cotton Spinners and Doublers Association was formed with Hector Christie as Vice-Chairman. Christie's continued spinning and weaving cotton at both mills until 1955 when they closed. Langcliffe Mill was bought by John Roberts and converted to papermaking.

Threaps Shed, Shed Mill or Watershed Mill, Langcliffe

Additional weaving capacity was achieved for Langcliffe Mill by building a single-storey weaving shed about half a mile to the south in 1840. This was enlarged in the late nineteenth century and early twentieth century. The original waterwheel was replaced with water turbines and these eventually gave way to a steam engine. In 1849 the new weaving shed, which was called Threaps Shed, and now known as Watershed Mill, held 103 7/8 looms, 91 4/4 looms, 48 7/8 looms and 112 4/4 looms with cylinders, though it was said it could hold 400 looms. The shed was owned by Richard Bashall and taken by Scott & Holden in 1852. After an idle period of several years in the later 1850s, textile production continued with this mill and Langcliffe Mill still being run together this time by the Christie family. Production stopped in 1955 and the building is now used as a retail outlet.

Watershed Mill, Settle

Catteral Hall Mill, Giggleswick

Catteral Hall Corn Mill was for sale in 1793 and was said to be 'well situated for erecting extensive works for spinning cotton, wool or flax'. Taylor & Son were listed as cotton spinners shortly afterwards and the mill may have been occupied by Davidson & Co. until the 1820s.

Giggleswick Mill

The corn mill here was advertised for sale in the 1780s and 1790s and the site was taken by Birkbecks on which they built a cotton mill about 1793. The mill was then leased by Redmayne & Thornber who were cotton manufacturers. William Redmayne, who had been a calico manufacturer in Blackburn, moved to Settle where he died in June, 1805.

On the 21st December, 1816, Giggleswick Mill, said to be 'newly erected', was for sale and was occupied by William's sons Giles and Robert Redmayne, who had a mercer's shop in Settle market place. The mill was 'at present in full work and well supplied with hands at moderate wages'. The mill building was three storeys high and measured 69 ft by 36 ft with both a waterwheel and a 16 hp steam engine. The carding, preparation and spinning machinery included 18 throstles with 2,416 spindles. Water for the wheel was supplied by Giggleswick Tarn.

> Also, all that newly erected Cotton Mill, Called GIGGLESWICK MILL, Well supplied with Water from Giggleswick-Tarn, and heated with Steam Pipes; being Three Stories high, and Twenty-two Yards and Thirty-two Inches in Length, by Twelve Yards and Eight Inches in Breadth, with a good Water-wheel. Tumbling Shafts, large Going Gears, and Appurtenances to the same belonging.—Also, a good STEAM ENGINE, Sixteen Horse Power, with every thing complete.—Also, all the MACHINERY in the said Mill, most of which is nearly new, and all in perfect Repair; consisting of Eighteen Throstles, containing together 2416 Spindles, Four excellent Carding Engines, One Cotton Picking Engine, with all other necessary Preparations for Carding and Spinning Cotton Twist.—And also, all that Close, or Inclosure of Meadow GROUND, lying behind the said Mill, containing, in Statute Measure, 1A. 3R. 4P. or thereabouts, in the Occupation of the said Giles and Robert Redmayne.

Leeds Mercury, 21 December 1816

The reason for the sale was that the Redmaynes were bankrupt and had to assign all their property to John Birkbeck, the banker in Settle, John Hurst a cotton merchant in Manchester and William Clayton from Langcliffe. The mill may then have been demolished soon afterwards.

Stainforth Mill

The old corn mill was taken for cotton spinning in 1792 by a large partnership consisting of John Riley and Jeremiah Smith, who were local cotton manufacturers, Robert Calvert, John Steel and Ann Steel. The following year Redmayne & Armitstead had taken the mill and John Armitstead bought flyers from Hattersleys in Keighley in 1805 and 1806. There is no evidence that they enlarged the mill and as they moved to other mills, production probably stopped at the same time. By 1841 the tythe map marked the site as 'Old Mill'.

Wharfe Mill, Austwick

This mill was built by two Lancashire cotton spinners, Jeremiah Taylor and Robert Parkinson, on the site of a former corn mill. Because the goit for the old corn mill was too low for the new mill, water was taken in a trough on pillars. The partners bought the land in 1791 and the mill was ready for use in 1792.

The two men, who were also cotton manufacturers, became bankrupt in 1795 and their mill was sold. It was four storeys high and measured 60 ft by 36 ft with a 30 ft x 4 ft waterwheel. Though it was advertised as a cotton mill, there were also four flax-spinning frames as well as ten cotton frames with another two unfinished. The fluting engine in the workshop was used to construct new machinery. Included in the sale were three cottages and the corn mill at Lawkland, which had also been bought in 1791, possibly with cotton spinning in mind.

Robert Burrow, a mule spinner at Westhouse Mill, bought Austwick Mill and machinery in 1797 and insured everything for £1,000. In 1811 it was being run by Thomas Taylor and James Wolfenden.

Burrow offered the mill for sale or to let in 1816 and 1817, together with seven cottages. It was then being run by James Birley for preparing and spinning silk. It was being run a few years later by John Taylor & Sons, who were there until 1836, but probably still owned by the Burrows. By 1846 the mill was a ruin, possibly as the result of a fire.

Clapham Mill

Wigglesworth, Armitstead, Petty & Co. were running the mill by 1786 and the mill and contents were insured for £1,000 in 1789. Some time before 1791, George Armistead & Co. bought iron rods, bars and screws from Kirkstall Forge and in 1798 the partners bought rollers and spindles, possibly for new spinning frames. The partners were George Armitstead, a yeoman, Thomas Wigglesworth of Padside Hall, Hampsthwaite Parish, a flaxdresser, William Petty of Darley, also from Hampsthwaite, a bridle-bit maker and Ephraim Ellis from Dacre, in the same area, a joiner. The mill and its machinery were for sale in February 1807 together with Ingleton Cotton Mill. John Armitstead would show prospective purchasers around the mill. A cottage was included in the sale. The mill was not sold, but advertised again in 1823 until when it had been used by John Armitstead for throstle spinning and had a 12 – 14 hp waterwheel. There was also a house, other buildings and a garden. It later became a bobbin mill and then a sawmill.

Clapham Wood Hall Mill

This mill, two miles from Clapham, was advertised for sale in 1798:

All that new erected cotton mill, situate upon the said estate, with the right of water belonging thereto, and all the necessary implements and machinery for the spinning of cotton.

Anyone interested had to apply to James Thornber of Settle. It may have been built as a speculative venture and equipped with jennies. No other references have been found and it was later converted to a sawmill.

Ingleton Mill

An Ingleton corn mill turned to cotton in 1791 after its purchase by George Armitstead, a cotton spinner from Clapham, Ephraim Ellis, a joiner from Ripon, William Perry, a bridle-bit maker and Thomas Wigglesworth, a flax dresser, both from Hampsthwaite in Nidderdale. Iron to make machine parts was bought from Kirkstall Forge and the partners traded as George Armitstead & Co. However, before the mill was finished Armitstead died and his wife headed the names on the fire insurance policy in 1792. The Royal Exchange and Phoenix offices covered the mill and contents for £4,000, which indicates that it was a good size. The purchase of the disused Ingleton corn mill then brought an additional water supply.

Ingleton Cotton Mill and the machinery in it were for sale in February 1807 as well as Clapham Cotton Mill, so the two were still run by the Armitstead family. Benjamin Ellis would show prospective purchasers around the Ingleton Mill. Two cottages were included in the sale. It is possible that flax was also being spun at this mill for some years and in 1809 it was described as a flax mill when it was advertised. However, the spinning machinery offered for sale then consisted of 13 water frames with a total of 604 spindles. The waterwheel measured 18 ft by 9 ft. The Burrows from Westhouse Mill then took the mill, or at least part of it, for in 1814 George Burrow's cotton machinery was for sale in the part of the mill

> **CAPITAL MACHINERY.**
> **TO BE SOLD BY AUCTION,**
> At Ingleton Mill, in the County of York, on Tuesday, the Seventeenth Day of May Instant, at 10 o'Clock in the Forenoon.
>
> ALL the COTTON MACHINERY, in that Part of the Mill occupied by Mr. G. Burrow, consisting of Upright and Tumbling Shafts and Drums, 1 Cotton Dresser, 1 Blowing Machine, 7 single Carding Engines, each Cylinder 31 Inches over; 3 Drawing Frames, Three Boxes, with 3 Rollers in each Box; 5 Fly Frames, 23 Spindles, three Rollers in each. The above are Cast Iron Framing, and of the newest Construction. Ten Mules, containing 3356 Spindles, at 1¼ Inches distant. A large Quantity of Cans, Bobbins, Laths, Benches, Joiner's Tools, &c.
>
> N. B. The above Machinery is nearly new, and in good Condition.
>
> For Particulars apply to Mr. G. Burrow, Westhouse, near Ingleton aforesaid, who will direct a Person to shew the above.—May 2d, 1814.

Leeds Mercury, 7 May 1814

he occupied. He had been running ten mules with 3,336 spindles. Included in the sale were all the shafting, preparing machinery such as cards and workshop machinery. The mill had been conveyed to James Coates, a linen manufacturer of Kirkby Lonsdale, the year previously with the stipulation that Burrow could continue for another year. John Coates & Co. then converted the mill to spin flax.

In 1822 John Coates & Son were listed as flax and tow spinners, but some time before 1832 they had changed over to cotton spinning and power-loom weaving, without success for their machinery was for sale that year. They had been running eight throstles with 768 spindles, two pairs of mules with 976 spindles and 11 power-looms. They were bankrupt and among their creditors was James Upton of Sedbergh. The machinery was not sold and the creditors must have decided that it was in their best interests to allow John Coates to continue in business. New capital was brought in and by 1837 the firm traded as Coates & Wright, cotton spinners. A steam engine may have been added at this time.

On 1st April 1854 there was a serious fire at Ingleton Mill. Fortunately it was insured with the Norwich Union and Sun fire offices so the mill was rebuilt and re-equipped. The new four-storey building measured 100 ft by 42 ft with a much larger waterwheel measuring 30 ft by 12 ft. There was also a Peel, Williams & Co. steam engine and a gas works. The Coates family were unable to let the mill, though it was advertised for several years. It may then have been bought by the owner of Ingleton collieries, William Bracewell, who leased it to Levi Towler from Burton Mill. He is listed for 1881 with his son John possibly running the mill. However, in June of that year the machinery in the mill together with the unexpired

TO COTTON SPINNERS and Others.—To be SOLD by Private Treaty the whole of the Valuable COTTON SPINNING MACHINERY, WORKING PLANT, STOCK, STORES, &c., at Ingleton Mill, Ingleton; together with the Lease of the Mill for an unexpired term of years. The machinery, which is almost new, consists of two warping mills, fifty spinning frames, twenty-four carding engines, three drawing frames, two slubbing frames, three intermediates, seven roving frames, and two scutching machines; all by Walker and Hacking, of Bury. The mill is let at a low rental, and to which valuable water rights are attached. For further particulars and to treat apply to Thomas Chorlton, Esq., Solicitor, Brazennose-street, Manchester; or to Messrs. Butcher, Litton, and Pownall, Accountants, 69, Princess-street, Manchester.
F 10861

Leeds Mercury, 10 June 1881

years of the lease was for sale. The machinery included 24 carding engines and 50 spinning frames. By 1888 the mill was empty and remained so until about 1900, when a Mr Middleditch of Halsteads, Burton-in-Lonsdale refitted the mill to spin hemp. Another fire in October 1904 reduced the mill to ground level and textile production ended.

Westhouse Mill near Ingleton

I can remember looking for Westhouse Mill and, after asking for directions from a local lady, was told I needed the old lino factory. The site looked like a farm, but with a large warehouse. Later I found that the mill had been used to make lino for a few years, but was pulled down in 1920. Robert Burrow, a local man, built the mill here for cotton spinning on family land before 1793. Steam power was used at an early date as the stream to the mill was inadequate. In addition a separate warehouse incorporating two cottages was built, which was what I had seen. The three-storey mill measured 90 ft by 45 ft, which made it larger than the average Arkwright-type mill. Robert Burrow was also involved with other local mills. In 1795, he bought Austwick Mill, putting in his son John as manager, and leased part of Ingleton Mill in 1809, but his spinning machinery there was for sale in 1814. Westhouse Mill and contents were insured for £1,000 in 1797 with the Phoenix fire office, with the machinery being the most valuable asset at £450. Mule spinning continued at Westhouse Mill by the Burrow family until 1835 when some of the buildings were turned over to agricultural use. However, the mill must have remained ready for use as it was advertised to let for mule spinning in the *Blackburn Standard* in June 1843. The manufacture of oil cloth on the premises started in 1877 and finished in the 1920s.

Burton-in-Lonsdale Mill

Unusually for the area, this mill started as a cotton- and silk-spinning mill, probably in 1794 when Simpson, Dodson & Co. insured the building for £1,000. This insurance valuation increased as the mill was completed and by 1797 the total enterprise was insured for £4,600 with the Royal Exchange and Phoenix Fire Offices. The five-storey mill, which measured 78 ft by 35 ft, had a 16½ ft by 10 ft wheel and was offered for sale in 1800. The mill was said to be newly erected, substantial and well built. The range of buildings also included a counting house, picking room, smith's and joiner's shops, two houses, a barn and a cow house. The mill was sold to John Green with payments made in instalments, but he failed in 1807.

Following Green's failure Burton Mill was put up for sale again when it contained completed and part-built machinery. There were 14 twist frames with six unfinished and ten mules with eight unfinished. Silk spinning was not mentioned. By 1822 the mill had been taken by Henry Smithies & Sons, who were also cotton manufacturers. However,

Thomas Kidd, who was a flax and tow spinner, may have occupied part of the mill. Smithies continued at this mill until the 1850s, when it was taken by Richard Brown & Co., who also ran part of Langcliffe Mill in Settle. By 1881 it had been taken by Levi Towler, a cotton manufacturer who also ran Ingleton Mill. The mill was later demolished.

Wensleydale and Swaledale

Northern Dales

There were only a few mills in Wensleydale. The first three were built for cotton spinning in the 1780s, but changed to flax or wool. All the mills then served the local hand-knitting or handloom weaving industry or, if they were used for flax, became part of the Knaresborough/Cleveland linen industry. Wensleydale exemplifies the overlap of the cotton, flax and woollen industries and the way in which the mills could be used to process a range of fibres. Gayle Mill, Yore Mill and what is known as the Flax Mill in Askrigg were all built about 1784 at the height of the first boom in cotton mill construction. They brought a new industry to the valley which was superimposed on the established woollen industry which produced hand-knitted garments for merchants in London and other parts of the country. Cotton had captured the attention of entrepreneurs everywhere and the sites on Gayle Beck, the Aysgarth Falls on the river Ure and Askrigg Beck in Askrigg village illustrate the diversity of places where mills were built.

John Byng (later Fifth Viscount Torrington) visited Askrigg in the summer of 1792 and wrote in his diary that:

People live here to a great age … all are employ'd in knitting stockings, worsted and yarn, an idle work, for the workers go where they like, talk, saunter, and sit down. But now the cotton trade is coming in; and a cotton mill is built near the town.

The mills at Gayle and Askrigg were typical Arkwright-style mills, nearly identical in dimensions; and both changed to flax and then wool after a few decades. Both exist, and remind one of the spread of the early cotton industry. Further mills were built at Askrigg and Haverdale for woollen manufacture when that became mechanised. Two small buildings were also used for spinning silk.

During the seventeenth century hand knitting was well established throughout the Yorkshire Dales. However, when the western Dales became more accessible via the new turnpike road between Keighley and Kendal, hand knitting declined in the Settle and upper Ribblesdale areas and became confined to the more remote Dales. Carriers operating from Kirkby Stephen, Kendal and Richmond delivered the thick greasy wool, known as 'bump', to be spun and knitted, at the same time collecting the knitted stockings and other garments. When mill-spun yarn became available this was either brought in from the new industrial areas such as Bradford or spun at the local mills. The worsted yarn was used to knit a variety of garments other than stockings, particularly after knee-high stockings went out of fashion for men. Gloves, caps and waistcoats were widely made. The 1881 census for Hawes and the surrounding villages shows that more than 100 women were knitting 'Guernsey Frocks' or what we would call seamen's sweaters. Several hundred more were still knitting hosiery, among them many who had probably trained at one of the knitting schools in the area. For instance, in 1851 Isabella Iveson was described as a knitter and schoolmistress with nine knitters and scholars with a further five knitters and Sunday scholars.

Hand knitting was a valuable additional source of income for many people in the area as well as a full-time occupation for others. Children, miners on the way to and from work and, it has been suggested, church congregations, knitted. They wore a belt into which was tucked a knitting sheath or stick to hold one of the needles. Some examples of these can be seen in the Yorkshire Dales Museum at Hawes. Later V-bed and circular knitting machines, though still operated by hand, produced larger items such as jacket and waistcoat pieces. Some machines were operated in workshops rather like a small factory, for example, the one in Middleham.

In the mid-nineteenth century Bainbridge had many hand knitters, usually of stockings. In 1855 and later, George Coates was listed as a Manufacturer of Knit Hosiery and William Lawson a Wool Stocking Manufacturer. However, there was also a workhouse where the inhabitants were trained in different skills. There, in 1861, six men and women wove cotton cloth.

Textile occupations were common. For example, in Askrigg, in 1834 some villagers were engaged in wool combing, others in the manufacture of knit hosiery and several in flax dressing. A wool stapler and a wool merchant were still active in the village in 1891.

Yore Mill, Aysgarth

Fascinating correspondence relating to the building and early life of this mill can be found in the Birkbeck papers in Leeds. The seven early partners included William and John Birkbeck from Settle, who were later to have interests in several cotton, worsted and flax mills. Other partners included John Pratt, a gentleman and amateur jockey, Abraham Sutcliffe, an apothecary from Settle, Robert Dickinson, an engineer from Lancaster, John Harrison, a hosier from Hawes and Christopher Picard, a gentleman from Cowan Bridge. Because none had any experience of running a cotton mill, they approached William Winstanley who ran a cotton mill at Walton-le-Dale near Preston and he became the eighth partner. Winstanley suggested that local children who were to be employed in the new venture should be brought to his mill to learn the necessary skills while Yore Mill was being built.

The site for the mill took advantage of Aysgarth Falls, one of the best waterfalls in the region; and it is interesting that Birkbecks' new worsted mill at Linton on the River Wharfe also took advantage of the well-known falls there. Building started in 1784 and continued through the winter, followed by the installation of spinning frames which were made by William Moore from Clapham. Production finally started about April 1785, but the correspondence shows that the lack of experience by the partners resulted in production problems and returns which were well below those expected. Their hopes of recouping their initial investment within the first year were not realised. Pratt died in 1785, Sutcliffe left the partnership the following year, being prepared to lose money on his investment, but George Wray and John Harrison Junior then joined the others. In 1801 the firm traded as Winstanley, Harrison & Co. when their stock and machinery was insured for £3,500. Much of the yarn was sent to Settle, perhaps to be woven by the handloom weavers there or it may have been sent to Manchester.

The partners decided to sell the building in 1811 and it can be seen from the advertisement in the *Leeds Intelligencer* that the original Yore Mill was built to the Arkwright pattern. It measured 57 ft by 27 ft, was four storeys high and had a counting house. Though it was said that the mill would hold double the amount of machinery it was, at that time, running 864 spindles on 14 spinning frames which were probably the originals. Application to view the mill had to be made to Mr Winstanley who lived at Redmire, but the partners were also prepared to let the mill. It would seem that the mill was not sold for it was advertised again in 1814. The same cards, drawing and spinning frames were still being used and it was stressed that the mill was near four villages which would have been a source of labour, John Halliday, possibly the manager, would show people round the mill, but application had to be made to Woodcock Winstanley. Yore Mill may not have been sold but then went out of use for some years.

The Rev T D Whitaker, in his *History of Richmondshire* published in 1822, recorded the demise of Yore Mill with some delight:

In my progress through this district I beheld many ruins with pleasure, but none, perhaps, with equal satisfaction to that which I experienced in the sight of a ruined cotton mill, which had once intruded itself upon this beautiful and sequestered scene.

However, it would seem that the mill was not in such a ruinous state. For a few years before 1829 the mill had been used for flax and tow spinning and the machinery which belonged to John Chippendale was for sale. Besides the preparing machinery there were three tow-spinning frames with

On Wednesday, the 27th Day of May, 1829, at YORE MILL, in Wensleydale, Parish of Aysgarth, County of York, the Property of Mr. John Chippendale,

FLAX and TOW MACHINERY; comprising Two Carding Engines, and One Sheet Card, with Frames, not being at work; Two Tow Spinning Frames, 32 Spindles each, 1½ Inch Travice; One Tow Spinning Frame, 34 Spindles, 3 Inch Travice; Preparings for the same; Five Spinning Frames for Flax, 32 Spindles each, 11 Inch Travice, for spinning fine Yarn; Two Spinning Frames, 32 Spindles each, 7½ Inch Travice; One Gill Roving Carriage, and other Preparings; Two Reels; a Quantity of Preparing Cans; a large Quantity of Spindles, 1½ Inch Travice, also of different Sizes.   JOHN DENT, Auctioneer.

Leeds Mercury 16 May 1829

88 spindles and seven flax frames with 224 spindles. The machinery was not sold and was advertised again in 1834. By that time the mill could also be bought or rented, although it looks as though it was used mainly for grinding corn with power from a 20 ft by 6 ft waterwheel. In 1851 it was again on the market, but as a corn mill. 'The mill was formerly used as a flax and cotton factory, and contains a portion of the machinery.' The resident owner was Mr Chippendale. At the same time a handbill advertising the sale mentioned that the upper two storeys had been used as a manufactory of worsted. This may have been the weaving of worsted cloth on handlooms. His desire to sell or rent the mill was thwarted in 1852 when the mill was burnt down. The Rev Mr Whitaker would have been pleased by that, but not by the subsequent rebuilding of Yore Mill at nearly twice the previous size.

Yore Mill, Aysgarth

Local bankers Other & Robinson bought the remains of the old mill and promptly built a five-story replacement. The lower storeys were used for corn milling while yarn for the local hand-knitting industry was carded and spun in the upper floors. This was probably a good-sized enterprise for nine woolcombers were at work in Aysgarth. William Pearson, who had worked at Haverdale Mill, was the first manager. In 1861 his two daughters were described as bookkeepers and assistant managers at the woollen factory. One daughter married John Clark who later became manager. Yarn spun at the mill was distributed over a large area to be knit into stockings and jerseys. One story from that time is that a large quantity of surplus jerseys were dyed red and sold to Italy to clothe Garibaldi's Red Shirts. From the size of the mill and the number of hand knitters in the area it is possible that jerseys could have been sold through merchants to Italy. It was not unusual for West Riding manufacturers to claim that in many European wars they provided clothing for both sides. Production of knitting yarn finished about 1870, but the mill continued as a corn mill. In 1893 the Yore Roller Flour Mill Company ran the mill and produced oatmeal and bread meal.

Askrigg Flax Mill

Early in March 1789 the *Leeds Intelligencer* carried an advertisement for the auction of Askrigg Cotton Mill on the 24th of that month. It was said that the auction of the lease was by consent of the respective proprietors and that besides the mill and machinery there was some land. The mill was described as being 'well adapted for being converted to any of the branches of machine spinning'. It seems odd that the advertisement should mention that the auction was with the consent of the proprietors, as that might appear to be obvious. However, since the start of construction in 1784 there had been problems between the partners. Originally these had been John Dinsdale, a country gentleman from Nappa Hall, John Driver from Askrigg, an attorney, and his brother Joseph Driver, who came from Keighley and was the only one who knew anything about cotton spinning. The three partners subscribed £1,000 each to this new venture. Two years later, when it was insured for £1,000 with the Royal Exchange fire office, it had debts of £2,500. The partners then quarrelled, with Joseph Driver returning to Keighley to take over part of Castle Mill. John Driver thought that he had bought out the other partners, but Dinsdale disagreed and took yarn spun at the mill from a cart on its way to Manchester. Though John Driver told the workmen to prevent Dinsdale entering the mill, this obstruction stopped when Driver died a few months later. John Dinsdale then took over the mill, with help from his men, and tried to collect all the outstanding debts. In 1788 the affair went to arbitration, but Dinsdale was declared a bankrupt within a short while. John Driver's widow Agnes bought the lease and stock, and brought back her brother-in-law to help her run the mill. She continued to have some control over the mill for several years. She married Abraham Hastwell, and in 1803 and 1804 they bought various items from Hattersleys of Keighley, including roving spindles.

Askrigg Flax Mill

The end of cotton spinning at Askrigg. Sale notice and elevation of 1814. [Yorks. Arch. Soc.: MD250/6]]

In 1814 the three-storey mill was put up for sale again. At the time it measured 56 ft by 30 ft and had a 'capital' waterwheel. Either after this sale, or within a few more years, the mill was changed from cotton to flax, and flax spinning continued with Joseph Siddell, a flax dresser and spinner, listed in a trade directory for 1834. By 1843 flax spinning had stopped, and John Hastwell sold the building to the Rev Richard Wood who made it into a house.

In the early part of the nineteenth century Mrs Hastwell was also running Low Mill, just a little downstream and near the road.

Askrigg Low Mill

This mill was built by Agnes Hastwell in 1803. At the time she was running the cotton mill further up the valley but Low Mill was built for woollen carding and some other processes which needed power. It was a small mill, only two storeys high, with the main rooms measuring 36 ft by 24 ft but with a two-storey extension used for dyeing. The mill was said to be 'nearly new' in 1815, and well adapted for worsted, cotton or flax. To tempt purchasers it was said that 'no advance will be required for the machinery in use at present'. However,

ASKRIGG, IN WENSLEYDALE.

TO BE SOLD OR LET, and entered at Pleasure,—All that Well-built WATER MILL, now employed in the Woollen Trade, Two Stories high, each Room 36 Feet by 24 within, and a Room at the End where Fulling Stocks are wrought.

The above Mill is pleasantly situated, and offers peculiar Advantages, as there is a good Supply of Water, and Work People may be had on reasonable Terms: and the Whole or a Part may be employed to great Interest in preparing the Wool and manufacturing Yarn for the Hosiers.—Apply to Mrs. Hastwell, Askrigg; if by Letter Post-paid.

Leeds Mercury 12 April 1823

the seller did not say what the machinery was used for, though when the mill was put up for sale again in 1823 it was for woollen spinning and fulling, with the fulling stocks in a room at the end. The spinning would have been done on jennies which were hand machines. Some yarn went to the local hosiers while other yarn was used for weaving woollen cloth which was then brought back to the mill for fulling in the stocks. John Moorhouse was listed as a spinner and weaver in Askrigg in 1834. Mrs Hastwell was not able to sell Low Mill and after she died in 1835, John Blyth from Hawes bought Low Mill. The Blyths were warehousemen and hosiers in Hawes and London. By 1855 it had passed to Thomas Gill from Low Row. He continued as a woollen manufacturer at the mill until 1873.

Askrigg Low Mill

Local wool was used, and all processes for making it into plaids, rugs and horse cloths were carried out at the mill. In addition some yarn was spun for local people to knit into jerseys and stockings but later worsted yarn was bought in from Halifax. Marie Hartley and Joan Ingleby describe the work carried out by Thomas Gill and his family at Low Mill in their book *The Old Hand-Knitters of the Dales*, with yarn being spun on a jenny and woven on a handloom. The cloth was made into garments for the local farmers and shepherds. The stockings, which were available in blue-grey, brown drab or dirty white, were knit very large and then shrunk. Today we would refer to them as sea-boot socks. After 1873 the mill was being used by a saw and rake manufacturer, Thomas Weatherald.

Gayle Mill, near Hawes

Gayle Mill is a superb monument to the water spinners of the late eighteenth century. By this I mean that it was typical of early cotton mills whose owners copied Richard Arkwright's design. It certainly was not built with a licence from Arkwright. It originally measured 47½ ft by 28 ft within the walls and was three storeys high although, being on a slope, there were some lower rooms. It was built about 1784 for spinning cotton by Oswald and Thomas Routh who were local landowners and hosiers. Being a hosier meant that they bought wool, put it out to spin, and then put it out to knit into garments, which they sold. However, it is possible that the Rouths had already enlarged the former corn mill, which had been on the site, to use it for wool scribbling and fulling. Documents refer to a new mill being built in 1776 which would be early for a scribbling mill, but would have speeded up the preparation of wool for the Rouths' hosiery business. In addition their own fulling stocks would have been useful for shrinking and felting the stockings and garments they had made. The Rouths built houses in the village along Beckstones as well as combing and carding shops. Clints House in the middle was their home.

However, for many involved in existing textile trades in the early 1780s, a move into mechanised cotton spinning appeared to offer generous profits if a standard formula was followed. The Rouths knew little about cotton spinning, so when they made the decision to build Gayle Mill in 1784, they had to employ a manager and this new venture was probably carried on in addition to their established hosiery business. By 1789 there must have been problems for they decided to try to sell their mill or lease the premises if no purchaser could be found. The 22 ft waterwheel was being used to drive four spinning frames with 60 spindles each as well as all the carding and preparing machinery. The mill was probably not sold in 1789 for an indenture of 1806 relates to the lease of the mill to be used in the rising flax industry. By this time the opposition to new textile machinery had been overcome in Lancashire, the steam engine was more readily available and large new cotton-spinning

COTTON MILL to be SOLD,
Or if more agreeable,
LET to FARM on LEASE for a Term of Years.

ALL that COTTON MILL; at the Town of Gayle, within a Quarter of a Mile of the Market Town of Hawes, in Wensleydale, Yorkshire, situate in a populous Neighbourhood, and Plenty of Hands at low Wages, upon and commanding the whole of the River Sleddale, well watered, and never in Back Water, and at least equal in Situation to any Cotton Mill in the Kingdom. The said Mill is in Length 17 Yards, Breadth 10½ Yards, Height 11 Yards, and three Stories high new built, with large Sashed Windows, and covered with the best Wensleydale Slate, and contains at present four Spinning Frames, 60 Spindles each, with all other necessary Machinery and Utensils, with an over shot Water Wheel, 22 Feet diameter, Mill-wright Work stout and new.

The said Mill is Freehold, and for further Particulars apply to Oswald and Thomas Routh, in Gayle aforesaid, Owners of the same; or of S. Fothergill, Market-street-lane, in Manchester.

Manchester Mercury, July 21, 1789. Simon Fothergill, mentioned in the advertisement, was a linen draper and hosier.

mills were being built west of the Pennines. If the early water frames in Gayle Mill had not been updated they would have been out-of-date by 1806 and there is some evidence that the timber from some of them was used to make a new floor in the mill when cotton spinning stopped. The early cotton spinning frames had been adapted to spin flax and that industry was becoming well established in Nidderdale and the Washburn Valley to the east. Gayle Mill was leased by John Readman who was in partnership with Tristram and James Walker as flax spinners. Besides Gayle Mill they also occupied Kirk Bridge Mill, near Bedale, for flax spinning, although again it was an old established corn mill. It was described as a spinning shop so probably only jennies were used. This partnership lasted only a few years for they were bankrupt in 1813. The hearing was in Northallerton and the assignees were Richard Jackson, a merchant from Northallerton, Thomas Meeke, a gentleman from Maunby and Thomas Yeoman, a flax spinner from Osmotherley. As usual in those days, Readman's mahogany chairs and dining tables, looking glasses, carpets, pictures and feather beds were also sold. When the affairs of the partners were finally wound up their creditors were paid nine shillings (45p) in the pound.

Following the bankruptcy of Readman & Walkers, the Rouths took Gayle Mill back for their own use, this time to spin yarn for their hosiery business as mechanized woollen spinning was now well established. Thomas Routh had continued as a clothier, for in 1804 he had bought two houses in Gayle which were converted into a stable and wash-house for his woollen business. In 1822 O & C Routh were described as knit hose, cap and shirt manufactures, doubtless having the garments knit by the hundreds of hand-knitters in and around Gayle and Hawes.

An inventory of 1826 lists all the machinery and tools in use in the mill. It was then said to be a:

... mill or factory at Gayle now used for spinning woollen yarn, with the water and other wheels, tumbling shafts, carding engine, wool dressers, throw or lathe, vice, anvil, crane, weights and scales, desk, wood chest and oil box thereunto belonging ...

The mill had a carding engine and fulling stocks, but it is not clear what spinning machinery was used. The mill was leased to E & A Knowles, hosiers of Low Row in Swaledale in 1830. For some reason Gayle Mill was offered for rent or sale in the early 1840s as a worsted mill. E & A Knowles left Gayle Mill, but took the machinery to Haverdale Mill which was to be their new base. Whether textile production continued at Gayle Mill after this time is not known.

Hosiery and other hand-knitted garments continued to be produced in the area for several years with hand knitting providing a valuable second income for men and women. There was therefore still a local market for hand-knitting yarn. Miners and farm workers all carried their needles and a stock of yarn to work up, even when they were walking to work. Eventually the small hand-powered knitting machines used in small workshops and the larger power-driven machines in the new factories in the Midlands

Gayle Mill, near Hawes

brought prices down so much that hand knitting was uneconomic. It became cheaper to bring in yarn from Bradford so local spinning mills went out of use. Gayle Mill was taken by the Alderson family, perhaps about 1856, and turned over to a saw and woodworking mill. In 1893 William Alderson, who was a joiner and builder, was using it as a sawmill.

Hawes Mill

John Blythe, who manufactured knit hose, caps, shirts, jerseys, horse cloths and rugs, built the first woollen mill in Hawes at the south-east corner of the bridge in Hawes. It was turned into a dyehouse when a new mill was built on the other side of the bridge. Nearby houses built round a little square were called Dyer's Garth. Blythe's spun yarn for knitters but also wove cloth and linen sheets. John Blythe took Askrigg Low Mill in 1835 and installed his brother as manager, but continued at Hawes for some years.

By 1841 wool combing and hand knitting were important occupations in Hawes. Miles Little, Frances Morton and Christopher Thompson were all described as following those trades in that year while Joseph Siddall was a flax dresser and spinner. They in turn would provide work for handloom weavers and knitters.

About 1840 Hawes Mill was taken by James Smith & Son who were already manufacturers of the usual range of hosiery, sweaters and rugs. They were well established as woollen manufacturers, but were now able to spin their own yarn. The mill looked like a typical West Riding Mill with three storeys and rows of windows. In 1890 James Smith & Son employed about 400 home knitters and 15 to 20 in the mill working knitting machines. In 1893 James Smith and Sons were described as manufacturers of knit hosiery. A partner called Whitaker, who married into the family, joined the firm and James's sons continued in business until 1903 when the mill became a creamery.

Countersett Silk Mill

This small and unusual mill was built in 1793 for spinning waste silk. There is evidence of a waterwheel being used, but references are sparse. It is assumed that that the wheel was used to run some sort of carding engine with the rest of the throwing or spinning processes being carried out on hand machines. Another similar, but un-powered building can be seen at Burtersett where it has been referred to as the 'Old Silk Mill'.

Haverdale Mill, in Swaledale

In 1823 E & A Knowles were manufacturers of knit yarn hosiery at Low Row. The family came from the Keld area and established a small fulling mill on Haverdale Beck. Gorton Lodge in Low Row was the family house, but they also had another house called Paradise where garments were made up and collected to be taken to the fulling mill for shrinking and final washing. In 1835 they started to build Haverdale Mill for spinning worsted and this became the centre of their business activities when it started in production in December 1836. Previously they had leased Gayle Mill for a few years and also bought yarn from Hebblethwaite Hall Mill, but when Haverdale Mill was completed they moved their woollen machinery there. By 1841 the two sons, James and John Knowles were described as woollen manufacturers.

Haverdale Mill, near Low Row

Initially the mill was powered by a large overshot wheel which measured 38 ft by 6 ft and was said to have been made and assembled in the mill yard. The mill was built with two sections, one for woollen and one for worsted. Both had four rooms which measured 60 ft by 40 ft. Part of the mill was used for weaving the worsted yarn into carpets on handlooms, which appeared to generally be a man's job. By 1851 there were also a dye house, weaving rooms, warehouse, counting house, oil house, storehouse and boiler house. The latter held an eight hp steam boiler, which was used for heating the mill and the drying stoves. The dye house held a large black tin dye pan, one copper and four cast-iron pans made by the Bowling Iron Company of Bradford. The woollen section had preparing machinery consisting of two teasers, four scribblers, four cards and four billies with spinning done on a pair of mules with 548 spindles. Fulling was carried out with two pairs of fulling stocks with iron backs. The worsted section was used for spinning carpet yarn. Some parts of the mill premises were also used for corn milling.

The mill and machinery were offered for sale on 31st October 1851 at The Buck in Reeth, with the second sale lot being the Miners Arms with some land and four houses at Low Row. It would seem that the mill did not sell so it was advertised again with the auction to take place at the mill on November 27th 1851, this time with the millstones and corn milling equipment as the second lot.

E & A Knowles may not have sold the mill for the firm continued at the mill until about 1870. They continued to make carpets which were said to be 'of excellent quality' while the woollen yarn was used to make seamen's jerseys which were knitted large and then shrunk to the correct size. The machinery needed more power than could be provided by Haverdale Beck so a steam engine was added with coal brought from Tan Hill Collieries. After about 1870 the mill was just used for grinding corn, then as a meal store and later for occasional concerts. By 1904 the mill was in ruins and it was pulled down in the 1930s, though the chimney was left for some time.

Around Sedbergh

Sedbergh Area

Several cotton and woollen mills were built around Sedbergh from 1790 onwards. According to Baines's Directory for 1822,

The principal manufacture of Sedbergh is cotton, and there are two mills, at which a considerable number of persons are employed one of them belonging to the firm of Messrs John Upton & Son and the other to Mr Peter Taylor.

Cotton spinning and later woollen manufacturing continued in the area until recent times. There was an extensive handloom weaving industry until power-looms were introduced. Hand knitting was also widespread until the end of the nineteenth century. At least one weaving shop where a number of handloom weavers worked was set up in Sedbergh. Handloom weaving of linen was also common and outdoor galleries were sometimes built so that weaving could be carried out in a beneficial damp atmosphere. Railton Yard is the sole surviving example in Sedbergh.

Dent was famous for its hand knitters and there were two shops where knitters collected yarn and returned finished garments. One was for a Kendal firm and the other was for Joseph Dover at Farfield Mill. The local knitters in Dent were probably supplied by Bannister Dawson who was a worsted and stocking yarn manufacturer at Dee Mill. In 1834 John Blythe, a worsted hosiery manufacturer, had a warehouse in Dent, though his mill was in Hawes. Dent also had outdoor galleries for weaving.

Hand knitting had been a major occupation for men, women and children around Sedbergh, Garsdale and Dent for over 300 years. Different yarns were used for different garments: thick greasy yarn called 'bump' for some stockings and caps and a finer yarn for gloves with an intricate pattern. Among the garments were hats, caps, mittens, socks, waistcoats and jackets which were called frocks. Knitters were paid three old pence for knitting 'bump caps' for slaves in the West Indies. These were made from coarse worsted yarn.

Milthrop Mill, Sedbergh

In April 1790, Garforths & Sidgwick from Skipton leased Milthrop corn mill and later that year advertised for clockmakers, as textile machine makers were then known. Insurance on the new mill was taken out in 1792 when the mill was insured for £800 with utensils, stock, goods and machinery for £2,000. The following year utensils and stock in a warehouse near the mill were insured for £1,500. More land was bought in 1793 and 1796 to improve the water supply and insurance details for 1804 indicate that the mill was four storeys high. When Garforths & Sidgwick registered their mill with the magistrates in 1805, they said that they employed about twenty people, but no apprentices.

John and James Upton from nearby Birks Mill, who had previously been tenants at Milthrop, bought the property from Garforths & Sidgwick with a mortgage in 1812 when the mill and contents were insured for £4,000. Uptons had bought the mill, cottages and land for £4,750. By 1816 the total insurance cover was £6,000 and the machinery consisted of five pairs of mules with 2,520 spindles and 24 throstles with 2,350 spindles. The mortgage was then transferred to the Skipton bankers, Chippendale, Netherwood & Carr in 1817 and paid off by 1821. By that year the mill was lit by gas. Total insurance cover increased to £7,000 by 1828 and £8,000 by 1834. Upton was also running Goit Stock Mill near Bingley.

In 1841 John Upton died, leaving the mill to his son James. The main machinery at the mill then consisted of 28 carding engines and 50 throstles with 5,500 spindles. James Upton & Son were still using the mill for cotton spinning in 1848 when it was for sale. It was advertised again in 1849 together with a recent extension, warehouse, gas house, stable, cart house, two cottages and land. The 23 ft by 11 ft wheel powered 6,900 throstle spindles and 1,800 mule spindles. Besides the cotton mill there were a large house, 17 cottages and an estate. By this time the whole mortgage on all the property had been taken over by Thomas Wearing, a local JP. Apparently the reason for the sale at this time was that James Upton could not keep up his mortgage repayments.

In 1864 James Upton died and again the mill plus the estate were put up for sale. James Dover from Farfield Mill had been looking for a mill for his sons to start woollen manufacturing and he became the new owner, thus changing the mill from spinning cotton to spinning wool. This yarn was used locally for making a range of knitted garments such as socks, sweaters and Kilmarnock caps. James Junior, Richard and Robert took over the running of the mill with James outliving his brothers. Eventually they were producing little but horse blankets and horse collar checks and the mill closed in 1931. James died in 1935 and with trade in decline since the First World War, the property was offered for sale. When no buyer came forward, it was agreed that it would be sold for the value of the stone. However, before the demolition contractors moved in, the buildings were requisitioned by the Ministry of Aircraft Production at the start of the war as part of the policy of dispersing essential aircraft production to remote areas. From 1947 until 1949 it was taken by the Admiralty. Limited production did start again, but a fire destroyed the mill in the 1960s. Now there are houses on the site, but the line of the old mill goit can still be seen.

Milthrop Mill, Sedbergh

Birks Mill, near Sedbergh

In 1796 Charles Holme, a Kendal hosier and woollen manufacturer, built Birks Mill as an investment, but let it to William Faulkner Brown & Co. for spinning cotton. They were bankrupt by 1807 and the mill was then occupied by John Upton, also for spinning cotton from at least 1809. The mill with machinery and stock was insured for £2,000 in 1810 by James Upton & Son who, besides running Milthrop Mill near Sedbergh, also later ran Goit Stock Mill near Bingley from about 1834. Holme had not been able to repay his mortgage on the property and house so both were forfeited to Arthur Croxton, with Charles Holme now renting the mill. He sub-let to the Uptons, but retained part of the mill for his woollen manufacturing business. Ownership of the mill changed in the next few years and the mill, or part of it, was leased by Peter Taylor by 1822. A fire in 1826 made Taylor bankrupt, when all that was left was a small writing desk and some account books. The mill was rebuilt by James Upton and total insurance cover increased to £3,000 in 1834.

Birks Mill, near Sedbergh

In 1849 Birks Mill was for sale. It had been occupied by James Upton, but was now occupied by Thomas Wearing or his under-tenants. The sale included a house and garden suitable for a manager, three cottages, a barn and outbuildings. The mill had been substantially rebuilt within a few years, was lit by gas and warmed with steam. The ground floor measured 57 ft by 43 ft and there were three storeys and an attic. A two-storey warehouse adjoined measuring 41 ft by 26½ ft. The waterwheel was estimated to produce 30 hp and measured 18 ft by 12 ft. As an inducement it was stated that the mill was 'about four miles from Lowgill, a first-class station on the Lancaster and Carlisle Railway, where cotton is delivered from Liverpool at about 7d per cwt'.

It is not entirely clear what happened to Birks Mill in the following years. Thomas Wearing occupied the mill for some time, probably spinning worsted yarn for the local trade. Later it was tenanted by Thomas Harrison who was listed there as a stuff manufacturer in 1881. William & Richard Haresnape were listed as bobbin turners in Sedbergh in 1857 and may have occupied part of the mill. It was eventually bought by Dovers from Farfield in 1893 for spinning yarn. However, by 1909 textile production had stopped, although the machinery was not removed, with part of the mill occupied by William Wilson for making bobbins and brush heads. With modern additions, it has been used for food processing.

Hebblethwaite Hall Mill, Sedbergh

Robert Foster built this woollen mill about 1792 near the site of Burnt Mill

which ground corn. Foster was a Quaker and an ex-naval officer who possibly had a partner for the first year called Charles Holme. His son, Myles, took Joseph Dover, a hosier from Keswick, firstly as manager and then as a partner and in 1812 the mill was for sale as part of an estate which included a mansion house, farmhouse and 300 acres. Foster lived at Hebblethwaite Hall and advertised the mill as being 'well adapted for woollen manufacture' and on the turnpike from Brough to Kendal. The mill, three cottages and a farm were sold to Warwick Pearson in February the following year for £10,800 and then let to Joseph Dover. Joseph Dover & Son were listed as woollen manufacturers here in 1834 and then built Farfield Mill, moving there in 1837. No further references to textile production at this mill have been found.

Farfield Mill, Sedbergh

This mill was built in 1837 by Joseph Dover for spinning wool for the local knitting trade and to spin yarn for his business which was manufacturing woollen cloth. The knitted garments were brought back to the mill for dying and fulling. He and his sons had horse blankets and various types of woollen cloth woven by local weavers, particularly check fabric. Farfield Mill was larger and had better transport links than other local mills and later power looms were installed. Houses were built for the workers at Hall Bank and later the Dovers built villas for themselves. Joseph Dover & Sons were listed as Guernsey frock and cap and milled flannel manufacturers in 1841 and as check manufacturers in 1857.

In November 1863 the partnership of James and John Dover at Farfield Mills was dissolved with John buying James's half share. John then bought Milthrop Mill for his three sons, James, Richard and Robert. The inventory of machinery and goods at Farfield mill prepared for this division included looms, tenters, beams, scales, bobbins, horses, carts and goods in process of manufacture.

About 1890, knitting machines were installed with the garments finished by hand in the workers' homes. The Mill burned down in 1909, but was quickly rebuilt. Trade declined and the Dovers sold the mill in 1937 when it was bought by the Farfield Spinning Co. for spinning carpet yarn. During the Second World War it was used for engineering purposes, but in 1947 was handed back to the spinning company and was still in use in 1951. After a brief period there was a revival of textiles from the 1960s when Mealbank Woollens moved from Kendal and took the mill to produce fine dress material. It was then taken by Pennine Tweeds and finally Bryan Hinton to produce rugs and shawls. Commercial activities stopped in October 1992 when the mill and two Dobcross looms dating from 1934 were taken over by a trust. The building is now an Arts and Heritage Centre.

Howgill Mill, north-west of Sedbergh

A small mill was built here early in the nineteenth century, possibly for spinning cotton, but later for spinning yarn for the local knitting and woollen industry. By 1838 it was being run by William Greenwood Best, who was still listed as a woollen manufacturer in 1857.

Dee Mill, near Dent

A spinning mill was built on the river Dee below Cowgill Chapel early in the nineteenth century. The earliest owner or tenant listed was Dawson Bannister, who was described as a worsted and stocking yarn manufacturer in 1822. He was a customer of Hebblethwaite Hall Mill before 1837. Nearby was a weaving shop which has since been converted into cottages. Dee Mill was to let in 1841. The lease included the machinery for spinning woollen and worsted yarns and was for seven or fourteen years. The mill was three storeys high and measured 52 ft by 43 ft with an adjoining wash and dyehouse. The wheel, 18 ft by 2½ ft, was also used to power a pair of fulling stocks. The mill could be taken immediately and there was also a house and warehouse. It would seem that

> **DEE MILL.—TO BE LET, by PROPOSAL,** with the Machinery suitable for a Worsted and Woollen Manufactory, for a Term of Seven or Fourteen Years. The Ground Floor is 52 Feet by 43 Feet broad. The Building is 3 Stories high, with a Wash and Dyehouse thereto adjoining, with Three Dyeing Vessels. The Mill is worked by Water Power, having a good Water Wheel, the Diameter of the Wheel is 18 Feet by 2 Feet and a Half broad, with a Pair of Fulling stocks. The Mill may be entered upon immediately.
> Also a good DWELLING-HOUSE, with a Warehouse adjoining, may be entered upon the 14th May next.
> Proposals will be received by Edmund Bannister until the 15th of March, when the Taker will be declared.
> Cow Gill, Dent, Feb. 5, 1841.

Leeds Mercury, 20 February 1841

the rent was negotiable as Edmund Bannister was prepared to receive proposals. No further references have been found and now only a few foundation stones remain. The mill was in ruins by the 1890s.

Rash Mill, near Dent

This manorial corn mill was south of Sedbergh on the river Dee. A deed of 1799 mentions a newly-erected cotton carding and spinning mill then in the possession of John Bradley, but early in next century it had reverted to corn. Later it became a joiner's shop.

LOCATION, SUMMARY AND REFERENCES

Around Skipton

Draughton Mill. SE 040528. Location not found.
1798 - cotton - 1830?
LI Apr 30, 1798. July 8, 1799.
Eastby Mill, Embsay. SE 017544. Demolished.
1792 - cotton - 1900?
RE 23/130798. 1792. LI Feb 8, 1813. White 1837.
Primrose Mill, Embsay. SE 006537. Demolished. Housing on site.
1792 - cotton – 1815 – worsted - 1890.
LI Nov 11, 1793. LM Mar 3, 1815. Mar 8, 1823.
Sandbanks Mill or Embsay Mill, Embsay. SE 006534. Industrial and commercial use.
1792 – cotton – 1932 – rayon/various – 1990.
RE 23/130931, 1792. LI Oct 28, 1805. LM April 10, 1823.
Millholme Mill or Millholme Shed, Embsay. SE 005533. Demolished.
1792 – cotton – 1870 – cotton and worsted – 1875 – worsted and cashmere – 1900.
RE 26/132536, 1793. LM April 10, 1828.
Good Intent Mill, Embsay. SE 001544. Private House.
1800 – cotton – 1850.
LM Dec 7, 1839. April 20, 1844. March 20, 1852.
Whitfield Syke Mill, Embsay. SD 997547. Under Eastby Reservoir.
1795 – cotton – 1875.
RE 32A/180514, 1800. LI Nov 20, 1809. LM Oct 20, 1838.
Rilston Mill. SD 959579. Demolished.
1792 – cotton – 1803.
LI Mar 9, 1795. HJ Dec 12, 1803. Bolton Estates MS.
Hetton Mill. Site not located.
1790 – cotton – 1800. LI Mar 9, 1795. April 2, 1798.

Threaplands Mill. SD 985606. Some buildings and dam.

1800 – cotton – 1818.

RE 32A/176879, 1800. LM Feb 21, 1818.

Marton Mill. Location not found.

1800 – cotton – 1810.

RE 32A/187054, 1801. HJ Aug 19, 1809. Ingle 2004.

Airebank Mill, Gargrave. SD 940541. Still in use.

1791 – cotton – 1830 – cotton and worsted – 1845 – cotton – 1933 – cotton and synthetic – to date.

Sun CR 143/1007586, 1823. LM July 22, 1826. April 2, 1842. Pigot 1818. Baines 1822.

Low Mill or Goffa Mill, Gargrave. SD 932539. Private apartments.

1797 – cotton – 1830? – worsted – 1850.

RE 32A/179691, 1800. HJ Mar 8, 1806. LI Dec 16, 1811. April 30, 1842. July 19, 1845.

High Mill, Gargrave. SD 924539. Private apartments.

1791 – cotton – 1860.

RE 21/126824, 1792. Baines 1822. White 1837.

Bell Busk Mill, Coniston Cold. SD 905562. Demolished.

1794 – cotton – 1862 – silk – 1901.

Sun CR7 636029, 1794. LM Mar 13, 1841. FEC 1834.

Eshton Bridge Mill, Eshton. Site not located. Demolished.

1797 – cotton – 1798.

LI Dec 24, 1798.

Airton Mill. SD 903592. Private apartments.

1787 – cotton – 1900.

RE 32A/158649, 1797. LM April 10, 1824. Sharp, 1990.

Scalegill Mill, Kirkby Malham. SD 899616. Holiday apartments.

1791 – cotton – 1904.

RE 21/127132, 1792. LM Sept 9, 1828. Mar 3, 1848

Malham Mill. SD 898633. Demolished.

1785 – cotton – 1825.

Sun 340/523459, 1786. LI April 28, 1800.

Wharfedale and Littondale

Low Mill, Addingham. SE 092494. Mainly demolished. 1920s mill now apartments.
1787 – worsted – 1824 – cotton – C1870 – silk/various – 1976. 1999 – wool – 2004.
Sun CR 161/106009, 1827. LI Dec.31, 1810. LM Aug 19, 1820. May 11, 1822. Feb 13, 1841. Aug 28, 1841. FEC 1834. Mason 1989.

High Mill, Addingham. SE 081503. Part demolished. Private apartments.
1786 – cotton – 1787 cotton/worsted – 1795 – cotton/worsted/flax – 1833 – worsted – 1869 – silk – 1953.
RE 13/104521, 1787. LI Aug 18, 1794. Oct 16, 1797. LM May 11, 1822. Mar 18, 1843. Mason 1989.

Townhead Mill, Addingham. SE 073499. Small industrial units.
1799 – cotton – 1827 – worsted – 1918 – rayon – 1971.
Sun CR 27/ 693628/1799. LM Sept 2, 1820. Jan 9, 1841. Mason 1989.

Fentiman's Mill or Saw Mill, Addingham. SE 078498. Housing.
1802 – cotton – 1854.
RE 25/135978, 1793. LM Feb 19, 1825. Mar 21, 1829. Mason 1989.

Burnside Mill, Addingham. SE 074497. Apartments.
1886 – silk – 1948.
Mason 1989.

Wolseley Shed, Addingham. SE 073497. Demolished.
1880 – cotton – 1918 – rayon/cotton – 1959.
Mason 1989.

Barcroft Mill, Addingham. SE076496. Demolished.
1918 – rayon/cotton – 1945 – nylon – 1959.
Mason 1989.

Beamsley Mill. SE 077526. Private house.
*c.*1800 – cotton – *c.*1821.
LM Jan 3, 1818. May 26, 1821.

Hartlington Mill near Burnsall. SE 041609. Rebuilt as holiday apartments.
1789 – cotton – 1830 – worsted – *c.*1880.

RE 21/126598, 1792. RE 32A/173537, 1800. LI May 12, 1789. LM Jan 25, 1817. Feb 19, 1848. Cotton Mill Returns 1803-6.

Burnsall Mill SE 031611. Now cottages.

1804 – cotton – 1825.

Lodge, E. *A Wharfedale Village*. Burnsall 1994.

Skyreholme Mill near Appletreewick. SE 065603. Demolished.

c.1800 – cotton – 1860.

LM July 6, 1822. Jan 28, 1843. Sept 20, 1851. FEC 1834.

Hebden Mill. SE 027624. Demolished.

1792 – cotton – 1927.

RE 28 /143711, 1795. LI Mar 3, 1800. Jan 13, 1812. HJ April 25, 1807. LM June 9, 1821. Feb 1, 1840.

Linton Mill near Grassington. SE007632. Housing on site.

1787 – worsted – 1844 – cotton/worsted – 1912 – cotton/rayon – 1959.

LM May 4, 1839. April 29, 1843. Oct 17, 1846. Aug 23, 1855.

Grassington Low Mill. SE 007633. Private house.

1800 – cotton – 1840 – worsted – 1894.

LI June 11, 1804. LM May 4, 1839. April 29, 1843.

Scaw Gill Mill, Grassington. SE 000644. Private house.

1792? – cotton – 1809.

HJ April 24, 1809. LI June 28, 1813. LM Oct 3, 1818.

Kettlewell Mill. SE 970723. Demolished.

1805 – cotton – 1856.

FEC 1834. LM Aug 28, 1858

Arncliffe Mill. SD 930718. Top two floors removed. Private house.

1792 – cotton – 1875.

RE 21/126825, 1792. Sun 127/965003, 1820. LI July 20, 1801. LM Oct 18, 1785. Mar 3, 1815. Oct 15, 1842. FEC 1834.

Washburn Valley

Westhouse Mill, Blubberhouses. SE 168555. Demolished.
1797 – flax – 1850 – cotton – 1856 – silk – 1870.
LI Dec 3, 1798. LM June 6, 1817. Sept 9, 1820. Feb 18, 1843. Jennings 1967.

Low Mill, West End. SE 152578. Demolished.

1791 – cotton – 1805 – flax – 1880.

LM Sept 3, 1825. Nov 11, 1829. June 4, 1836. April 15, 1837. Jan 9, 1841. April 17, 1847. Jennings 1967.

Patrick's Mill or High Mill, West End. SE 144580. Demolished.

1800 – cotton – 1812 – flax – 1847.

Cotton Mill Returns 1803-6. Jennings 1967 LM March 20, 1852.

Little Mill, West End. SE 143580. Demolished.

1805 – cotton – 1822 – flax – 1841.

LI Mar 2, 1807. Crompton 1811. LM March 20, 1852.

High Mill or Croft House Factory or Aked's Mill, West End. SE 136582. Demolished.

1809 – flax – 1844.

LM May 25, 1816. Dec 4, 1824. Jan 2, 1836. Dec 11, 1841. Feb 1, 1845.

Around Settle

Fleet's Mill, Long Preston. SD 832575. Agricultural use as a barn.

1792 – cotton – c.1828.

RE 25/130999, 1792. LI Aug 3, 1812. Jan 24, 1814.

Lower Mill, Long Preston. SD 832575. Demolished.

1792 – cotton – c.1828.

LI Aug 3, 1812. Jan 24, 1814.

Rathmell Mill. Exact site not located. Workshop.

c.1795 – cotton – c.1810.

Aspin, 2003.

Runley Bridge Mill, Settle. SD 810622. Private house.

1786 – cotton – c.1847.

Sun 341/524976, 1786.

King's Mill or Snuff Mill, Settle. SD 814638. Private apartments.

1825 – cotton – 1847.

LM Aug 12, 1820. FEC 1834.

Scaleber or Dog Kennel Mill, Settle. SD 823631. Demolished.
1790 – cotton – *c*.1850.
Sun 12/648969, 1795.
Bridge End Mill, Settle. SD 817641. Private apartments.
1785 – cotton/worsted – 1800 – cotton – 1849.
LM 22nd Nov, 1785. LI 14th July, 1800.
Langcliffe Mill near Settle. SD 816650. Now paper.
1784 – cotton – 1955.
LM Sept 18, 1852.
Threap's Shed or Watershed Mill, near Settle. SD 818643. Retail outlet.
c.1840 - cotton – 1955.
LM 26th May, 1849.
Catteral Hall Mill. Exact site not located.
c.1795 – cotton – *c*.1820. Demolished.
LI 25th March, 1793.
Giggleswick Mill. Exact site not located.
c.1793 – cotton – *c*.1816. Demolished.
LM Dec 21, 1816.
Stainforth Mill. Possibly SD 818674
1792 – cotton – *c*.1810. Demolished.
Aspin, 2003.
Wharfe Mill, Austwick. SD 779692
1792 – cotton/flax – *c*.1826 – cotton/silk – *c*.1840. Demolished.
LI June 29, 1795. Feb 17, 1817. LM Oct 29, 1836. JA/25 WYAS, Leeds.
Clapham Mill. SD 030613. Sawmill (Possibly rebuilt).
1785 – cotton – 1823.
Sun OS 341/525298, 1786. LI Feb 9, 1807. YHQ. Vol 12. Summer 2007.
Clapham Wood Mill. Exact site not located.
1798 – cotton - *c*.1800. LI Aug 17, 1798. YHQ. Vol 12. Summer 2007.
Ingleton Mill. SD 694732. Demolished.
1791 – cotton/flax – *c*.1826 – cotton – 1904.
RE 23/130150, 1792. LI Feb 9, 1807. May 7, 1814. LM June 10, 1881. YHQ.
Vol 2. 1996.

Westhouse Mill near Ingleton. SD 670737. Mainly demolished.

1791 – cotton – *c.*1830.

LI Mar 2, 1812. Feb 17, 1817.

Burton-in-Lonsdale Mill. SD 652719. Demolished.

1794 – cotton/silk – 1807 – cotton – *c.*1890.

RE 29/648968, 1795. LI Sept 29, 1800.

Wensleydale and Swaledale

Yore Mill, Aysgarth. SE 010886. Now a museum.

1784 – cotton – *c.*1814. *c.*1825 – flax/cotton – 1852 – worsted – *c.*1870.

RE 13/102200, 1787. LI Nov 11, 1811. LM May 9, 1829. May 17, 1851.

Askrigg Flax Mill. SD 944910. Private house.

1784 – cotton – *c.*1814 – wool – *c.*1870.

RE 10/96349,1786. LI March 10, 1789. Oct 14, 1815.

Askrigg Low Mill. SD 945908. Private house.

1810 – wool – *c.*1890.

LM April 12, 1823.

Gayle Mill near Hawes. SD 871893. Heritage centre.

1784 – cotton – 1806 – flax – 1813 – wool – 1856.

LI Dec 20, 1813. Hartley & Ingleby 1953. Alderson 1980.

Hawes Mill. SD 873897. Demolished.

1840? – worsted – 1903.

Countersett Silk Mill near Bainbridge. SD 912871. Still standing.

1793 – silk – *c.*1800.

Tuke 1794

Haverdale Mill near Low Row. SD 976969. Demolished.

1835 – wool/worsted – *c.*1870.

LM Oct 11, 1851.

Around Sedbergh

Milthrop Mill near Sedbergh. SD 662912 Demolished.
1790 – cotton – 1864 – worsted – *c*.1960.
Sun 391/606854, 1792. LI Dec 28, 1790. LM Aug 30, 1848.
Birks Mill near Sedbergh. SD 651913. Future uncertain.
1796 – cotton – *c*.1850 – worsted – *c*.1909.
Sun CR 89/840140, 1810. LM Aug 22, 1849.
Hebblethwaite Hall Mill near Sedbergh. SD 693932. Demolished.
1792 – wool – 1837. LI Aug 17, 1812. Hartley & Ingleby 1951.
Farfield Mill near Sedbergh. SD 677919. Heritage and Arts Centre.
1837 - wool – 1992.
Giles & Goodall 1992.
Howgill Mill. SD 633950. Private House.
c.1800 – cotton?/wool – *c*.1860.
Dee Mill near Dent. SD 752868. Demolished.
c.1810 – wool – *c*.1841 – worsted and cotton – *c*.1860.
LM Feb 13, 1841.
Rash Mill near Dent. SD 658899. Demolished.
1799 – cotton – *c*.1810.

[Abbreviations: FEC: Factories Enquiries Commissioners; HJ: Halifax Journal; LI: Leeds Intelligencer; LM: Leeds Mercury; RE: Royal Exchange (fire policy registers); Sun: Sun Insurance (fire policy registers); WYAS: West Yorkshire Archive Service.]

Bibliography

Official publications
1833 (450) XX, 1833 (519) XXI, 1834 (167) XIX and XX, Reports from Commissioners appointed to collect information in the Manufacturing Districts, relative to Employment of Children in Factories.

Newspapers and periodicals
Halifax Journal, Ilkley Gazette, Leeds Intelligencer, Leeds Mercury.

Trade Directories
Barfoot, P. and Wilkes, J., *Universal British Directory*, 5 vols. (1791-7)
Baines 1822. Pigot 1828/9. White 1837. Pigot 1841. White 1853. Slater 1855.
White 1866. Kelly 1881. Post Office 1891. White 1894.

Private Textile Mill Surveys Including Yorkshire
Colquehoun 1788. Crompton 1811.

Manuscript Collections
Birmingham Public Library. Boulton & Watt collection.
Brotherton Library, University of Leeds. Marriner collection.
Guildhall Library, London. Sun Insurance Company, fire policy registers.
    Royal Exchange Assurance Company, fire policy registers.
Kirkstall Forge, Leeds. Sales ledgers.
North Yorkshire County Record Office, Northallerton. Langcliffe Mill accounts.
West Yorkshire Archive Service, Bradford. Hattersley Papers.
West Yorkshire Archive Service, Leeds. William Vavasour's diaries.
West Yorkshire Archive Service, Wakefield. Factory returns (1803 – 06).
Yorkshire Archaeological Society, Leeds. Askrigg Mill papers.

Books and articles

Aitkin, J., *A Description of the Country from Thirty to Forty Miles Round Manchester* (1795)

Aspin, C., *The Water Spinners* (Helmshore 2003)

– *The Cotton Industry* (1981)

Baines, E., *The History of the Cotton Manufacture in Great Britain* (1835)

Baines, E., History, Directory and Gazeteer of the County of York (1822) vols. 1 and 2

Bentley, J., *Old Ingleton* (1976)

Brayshaw, T. and Robinson, R.M., *A History of the Ancient Parish of Giggleswick* (1932)

Brown, G. H., *On Foot Round Settle* (1896)

Byng, J., *The Torrington Diaries, 1781-1794* (1935)

Chapman, S. D., The Arkwright Mills – Colquhoun's Census of 1788 and archaeological evidence, *Industrial Archaeology Review*, 6 (1981 -2)

Curtis, S. J. and M. E. A. Boultwood, *An Introductory History of English Education Since 1800* (1965)

Giles, C. and Goodall, I.H., *Yorkshire Textile Mills* (1992)

Hare, C., *A Walk Around Kettlewell* (Kettlewell, 2002)

Hartley, M. and Ingleby, J., *Yorkshire Village* (1953)

Hartley, M. and Ingleby, J., *The Old Hand-Knitters of the Dales* (Clapham, 1951)

Hodgson, J., *Textile Manufacture in Keighley* (Keighley, 1879). Facsimile reprint with an introduction and index by Gillian Cookson and George Ingle (Stamford, 1999)

Ingle, G., *Marriner's Yarns* (Lancaster, 2004)

Ingle, G., *Yorkshire Cotton* (Preston, 1997)

James, J., *History of the Worsted Manufacture in England, from the Earliest Times* (1857)

Jenkins, D.T., *The West Riding Wool Textile Industry 1770-1835* (1975)

Jenkins, D.T. and Ponting, K. G., *The British Wool Textile Industry, 1770-1850,* (1982)

Jennings, B. (ed), *A History of Nidderdale* (Huddersfield, 1967)

Joy, D. (ed), *Hebden* (Skipton 2002)

Lamb, M., *The Story of Farfield Mill Restoration* (Sedbergh, 2008)

Mason, K. M., *Woolcombers, Worsteds and Watermills* (Addingham, 1989)

Mason, K. M., Addingham (Addingham 1996)

Raistrick, A., *Old Yorkshire Dales* (1967)

– *The Pennine Dales* (1970)

Riley, F. *The Settle District and North-West Yorkshire Dales*. Settle, 1923

Roberts, D., *The Development of the Textile Industry in the West Craven and the Skipton District of Yorkshire*, MSc dissertation, LSE (1956)

Sharp, W., *A History of Airton Mill.* (Skipton, 1990)

Shutt, G., *Wharfedale Water Mills.* Unpublished MPhil thesis, (Leeds, 1979)

Speight, H., *The Craven and North-West Yorkshire Highlands* (1892)

Speight, H., *Upper Wharfedale* (1900)

Tuke, J., *General View of the Agriculture of the North Riding* (1794)

INDEX

*References in **bold** are to illustrations.*

Broadley, William, 6
Brough, 170
Brown, James & Co, 33, 98
Brown, John, 74
Brown, Lee, 56
Brown, Richard, 15
Brown, Richard & Co, 138, 147
Broughton, near Skipton, 53
Buck, Thomas, 116, 134
Buck, William, 48, 134
Buckden, 81
Burley-in-Wharfedale, 81
Burnley, 17
Burnsall, 6, 23, 28, 98
Burrow, George, 143
Burrow, Robert, 141, 142, 145
Burtersett, 17, 40, **40**
Burton-in-Lonsdale, 17, 36
Byng, John (later Viscount Torrington), 148

Calderdale, 1
Calvert, Richard, 48
Calvert R & W, 111
Carr & Chippendale, 58
Catterick, 17
Chamberlain, G & A, 58
Chamberlain, William, 57
Cheshire, 13, 14, 15, 85
Chester, Richard, 102, 111
Chippendale, John, 151, 152
Chippendale, Netherwood & Carr, 118, 119, 120, 166
Clapham, 49
Clayton, William, 33, 130, 134, 141
Clayton & Walshman, 20, 28, 34, 35, 47, 135, 136, 137
Claytons & Wilson, 137
Cleveland, 5, 7
Clark, John, 153
Cliffe, James, 50, 112, 113
Clitheroe, 68
Cloth Halls, 10
Coates, George, 149
Coates, J & Sons, 144
Coates & Wright, 144
Cockroft, John & Sons, 92-93
Cockshott, John, 16, 48, 82, 83, 89, 92, 104
Cockshott, William, 50
Cockshutt & Co, 79
Colbeck, Thomas, 30, 31, 118, 119
Colbeck & Co, 30, 48, 118, 119

Collyer, Robert, 31
Colne, 17, 85, 114
Combing:
    hand, 9, 14, 16
    machine, 86
Congleton, 39
Coniston, 28
Conistone, 6, 36
Cononley, 3, 62
Constantine, Joseph, 103
Corlas & Co, 77
Courtaulds, 41, 62
Cowan Bridge, 150
Cowgill Chapel, 172
Cowling, 107
Craven, 11, 13, 129
Craven Navigation Company, 55
Cray, 81
Crompton, Samuel, 126
Cross, John, 24
Crossley, Thomas, 13
Crowther & Co, 121
Croxton, Arthur, 168
Cunliffe, Ellis, 84
Cunliffe, John, 16, 82, 83, 104
Cunliffe & Gill, 83

Danson, Thomas & Co, 34
Davidson & Co, 140
Dean, Ambrose, 48, 82, 92
Dean, John, 92
Dearlove, Robert, 125
Demaine, William, 49, 116
Dent, 2, 7
Derbyshire, 13
Dewhurst & Co, 61, 62, 76, 77, 78
Dewhurst, James, 67
Dewhurst, John, 130
Dewhurst, Thomas, 56
Dickinson, Robert, 47, 150
Dinsdale, John, 153, 154
Dockroy & Pinder, 125
Dolphinholme, 16
Dover, J R & R, 169, 170
Dover, James, 167
Dover, Joseph, 165, 169, 170
Draughton, 3, 36
Driver, Agnes, 20, 154
Driver, John, 153, 154
Driver, Joseph, 153, 154

Lightning Source UK Ltd.
Milton Keynes UK
12 September 2009

143604UK00002B/1/P